Fruit

AN ILLUSTRATED HISTORY

p.4 A stylised pineapple illustration from *Nurnbergische Hesperides*,
by Johann Volckamer, published in 1700.

First published by Scriptum Editions
565 Fulham Road, London SW6 1ES
in association with The Royal Horticultural Society.

Created by Co & Bear Productions (UK) Ltd.
Copyright © 2002 Co & Bear Productions (UK) Ltd.
Text copyright © Co & Bear Productions (UK) Ltd.
Co & Bear Productions (UK) Ltd. identify Peter Blackburne-Maze as author of the work.
Preface copyright © Brian F. Self. Brian F. Self asserts his moral rights.
Photographs and illustrations copyright © The Royal Horticultural Society, Lindley Library.

Publishers Beatrice Vincenzini & Francesco Venturi
Executive Director David Shannon
Art Director Pritty Ramjee
Designer Karen Watts
Publishing Assistant Ruth Deary

Printed and bound in Italy, at Officine Grafiche DeAgostini.

First edition
10 9 8 7 6 5 4 3 2 1

ISBN 1-902686-14-4

Fruit

AN ILLUSTRATED HISTORY

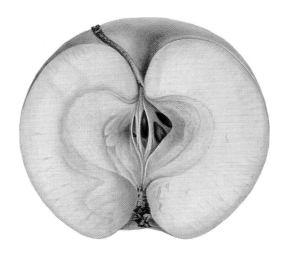

Written by Peter Blackburne-Maze

with a preface by Brian F. Self

THE ROYAL HORTICULTURAL SOCIETY

SCRIPTUM EDITIONS

Contents

Preface

Fruit was collected long before it was brought into cultivation, and its history and evolution provide a fascinating story. Fruit is such a vital part of our daily diet, adding both colour and flavour to food, that we may sometimes need to be reminded of this fact.

I have known Peter Blackburne-Maze, author of *Fruit: An Illustrated History*, since he was a student at Writtle College. In the intervening years he has moved in a variety of horticultural spheres, gaining experience as a fruit grower, manager, technician and adviser before establishing himself as a writer and journalist. In these roles he has shown a passion for fruit and, importantly, encouraged others to share his interest. Peter has worked with me in my capacity as chair of the Royal Horticultural Society's Fruit and Vegetable Committee, and I have served under his enlightened chairmanship of the Society's Fruit Group Committee.

The reader of *Fruit* will soon appreciate that Peter is a total fruit enthusiast. In the book, he has carefully distilled a wealth of information on the botanical history and culture of fruit, and presented it (as I imagined he would) in a very readable form, in one, single volume. He describes where many of our fruits originated – for example, the apricot, *Prunus armeniaca*, originated in China, not (as its name might lead us to assume) Armenia. Peter also includes references to fruit in Greek mythology; describes the winning role of 'golden apples' (supplied by the goddess Aphrodite) in an athletic contest; and outlines how many indigenous species were involved in the development of the modern fruit varieties grown by commercial and amateur horticulturalists today.

All who know Peter will be familiar with his sense of humour, and his colourful character certainly lightens the text. The illustrations dominate the book, but this is by no means a criticism – the celebrated botanist and horticultural artist William Hooker, and the lesser-known Victorian pomologist Robert Hogg, would be delighted to see some of their masterly illustrations given such prominence in this publication. The book's large colour illustrations (selected from the archives of the Royal Horticultural Society's Lindley Library) are striking, lavish and superbly reproduced.

I would recommend *Fruit* just as much to the ordinary reader (who is perhaps not so well versed in fruit matters) as to the dedicated fruit enthusiast. Either way, it will surely encourage interest in the subject. This magnum opus is an appreciation of fruit – a book to dip into, to savour and to enjoy.

BRIAN F. SELF

OPPOSITE: The frontispiece from *Traite des Arbres Fruitiers*, by Henri Duhamel du Monceau, published in 1768.

Introduction

We can all list a range of different fruit – apples, pears, plums, bananas and oranges immediately spring to mind, for example. From a botanical point of view, however, a fruit is defined as a 'more or less fleshy pod, capsule or some other body produced by a plant in which it forms and carries its seeds'. The flesh makes the fruit look attractive to eat, and this helps seed distribution. Indeed, many a good seedling fruit tree started its life as a core or stone thrown from a car window and onto a fertile road verge. The feature of sweetness isn't crucial to the definition of a fruit (tomatoes, cucumbers and marrows are all perfectly good fruit), but in the popular sense of the word a 'fruit' has to be sweet, and this is the definition we will use in this book.

HOW IT ALL BEGAN

All the fruits in cultivation today are selections, mutations, hybrids or descendants of genera and species that originally grew in the wild. Prehistoric fruity remains have been found all round the world, including seeds of wild strawberry, raspberry, blackberry, sloe, bird cherry and crab apple. The spread of wild fruits in the world's temperate regions was dependent on the movement of the ice caps: as the earth's temperature rose, growing conditions improved. And, in the warmer regions, natural seed dissemination and other methods of propagation further promoted the spread of wild fruits across the globe.

The presence or absence of naturally growing food has largely dictated the advance of human beings into previously unpopulated areas. It is only comparatively recently that settlers have brought their own food plants with them. This phenomenon has taken place throughout the ages, and nowadays there are very few people in the world reliant on naturally occurring foodstuffs.

More than five thousand years ago (perhaps even earlier), the climate was favourable for agriculture, so huge areas were cultivated. Most temperate fruits originated from Central Asia and what was then Asia Minor – the Caucasus, Turkestan and the Black Sea region – where vast areas of woodland with wild pears, crab apples and cherry plums still exist (indeed, some of the wild grapes in Central Asia are identical to today's cultivated varieties). Further afield, there are quinces in Azerbaijan, apricots in Armenia and Syria, along with cherry plums, bird cherries and medlars.

This abundance of natural food in what became known as the Fertile Crescent (reaching from Iran to south of the

A GARDEN WITH WATTLE FENCE

OPPOSITE: An early illustration of a medieval garden surrounded by a wattle fence, taken from Sir Frank Crisp's (1843–1919), 'Medieval Gardens', which was published in 1924.

Caspian Sea, to Turkey, through Palestine and into Egypt) encouraged nomadic tribes to settle in the area. This often brought new blood into an already flourishing civilization, therefore improving it further. During this period, the peach (*Prunus persica*) came from China (not Persia), where it has now been cultivated for more than 4000 years.

The first fruit to be stored for any length of time was probably the plum. These would have been sun-dried and then packed away for future use. Apples, too, were stored. They could have been dried as well, but were also laid on straw and placed in dry and cool surroundings.

Certainly as far back as 500 BC, Ancient Greek and Roman writers were writing about fruit and wine. Already both cultures were raising fruit, as well as growing vines from cuttings, and even then it was known that this kind of vegetative propagation was necessary amongst fruit plants in order to produce progeny identical to that of the parent. About two thousand years ago, fruit had become a highly important crop throughout the Mediterranean area. Excavations have shown pottery, glass, even the walls of houses, decorated with fruits. Evidence of orchards, nurseries and fruit markets were plentiful around Pompeii and Herculaneum, for example. Before the devastating eruption of Mount Vesuvius in AD 79, the slopes of the volcano were home to thriving horticultural and viticultural industries.

It was also around this time that varietal names started to appear. Many European fruit-growing practices started during the times of Roman occupation – the English, for example, had little knowledge of horticulture or agriculture until the Romans occupied the country. After the Romans left (in AD 410), English growers returned almost to the wild for seven hundred years, but then the Normans invaded and got the fruit trade on its feet again, a situation that was partly aided by the self-sufficient monasteries.

The big explosion, however, came with the spread of fruit cultivation from Europe to the rest of the world (and the United States in particular). Once North America, Australia and Australasia were discovered and colonized, things simply snowballed on a global scale. This fact is prominent in most of the early books on fruit growing – the further back you go, the more familiar the fruit varieties and methods of cultivation seem to become. North America and Australasia, once (literally) put on the map, soon became the founts of knowledge on the subject.

The original settlers carried with them a sort of skeleton agriculture (including horticulture), which would see them through the first all-important years of colonization. Once the trauma of setting up a community in a new and totally isolated land (often complete with unfriendly local inhabitants) had been overcome, more time could then be spent on 'research and development'. This involved searching for local species of familiar plants and either taming them with cultivation or using them to breed locally desirable characteristics into existing varieties. Here, one often comes across occa-

sions where the pupil overtakes the tutor, and the modern North American apple industry is a prime example. Of all the varieties bred in the USA during the last hundred years or so, most are eaten all over the world and many are also grown there – for example, 'Golden Delicious', 'McIntosh, 'Jonathan', 'Jonagold', 'Red Delicious' and many more.

METHODS OF PROPAGATION

Seeds are the most common and cheapest way to grow a large number of plants quickly. However, seed is only useful when it gives rise to plants that are virtually identical to the parent. Although this is quite easily achieved with flowers and vegetables, it simply isn't possible with tree and bush fruits, whose progeny, when grown from seeds, seldom bears any resemblance to the parent. Any of the ancestors of an individual modern hybrid variety are likely to appear in the seedlings and normally it is the oldest genes that are the most dominant.

With vegetative propagation, part of the plant you wish to propagate is detached and is encouraged to form roots

THE ORANGERIE AT VERSAILLES
ABOVE: An illustration of the Orangerie at Versaillés, from the *Treatise on Orange Trees* by Jean de la Quintinye, of 1693.

ETCHING OF TREE GRAFTING

ABOVE: An early illustration depicting the art of tree grafting, from the first published work of the writer Leonard Mascall, *Of the Arte and Maner Howe to Plant and Graffe all Sortes of Trees*, which was published in 1572.

and develop into another plant. Most bush fruits, for example, are propagated from stem cuttings, but unfortunately cuttings from tree fruits do not root readily. It was the Romans who found the answer. Tree fruits, then and now, are propagated most easily and successfully by budding or grafting. A rootstock (a ready-made root system) and a 'scion' (a piece of the tree you are propagating) are joined and bound together. In a short time they fuse, and buds on the scion start to grow, eventually forming the new tree. And, because this is formed from part of the original tree, it is absolutely identical to it.

Later on, this gave rise to a peculiar belief that an individual variety of fruit had a predetermined life expectancy. According to this theory, when a seed germinated and grew into a new variety, an imaginary internal clock started ticking and continued to do so in all the progeny raised from it. This ticking would continue through the generations – until, say, a hundred years had passed after the 'birth' of the variety, when all its living descendants dropped dead and the variety was extinct. Such a theory is completely false, although not quite as stupid as it might sound, because something similar does actually occur with the bamboo, which has such an 'alarm clock' that goes off when it flowers. All the offspring of any particular bamboo plant will flower at more or less the same time, then it will die, no matter how young or old the offspring are.

BREEDING NEW VARIETIES
Once vegetative propagation had become established, it meant that new varieties could be multiplied reliably. This was a gigantic leap forward, because at last the door was open to growing and propagating varieties of fruit which were better (in quality, size, appearance, health and performance) than existing ones – the main aim of modern plant breeding.

Not too long ago, how a fruit tasted came pretty low down on the list of priorities; what mattered to the consumer was its appearance and size. But, if people choose larger (and less tasty) apples over smaller (and possibly better-flavoured) ones, the lack of demand for the latter will lead to their eventual disappearance. It is completely wrong to blame the retailers, because they will only stock what they can sell. Mercifully, however, flavour is back in fashion. One of the main horticultural aims today is to breed new varieties with resistance to important pests and diseases. The growers want this because it would reduce production costs, and the consumers do because there is an increasing level of 'zero tolerance' towards pesticide residues.

These new features have to be incorporated without losing any of the existing desirable characteristics, however. And this is where genetic modification (GM) would have an incalculable advantage over the traditional sexual way of producing new varieties. Using GM, a plant breeder could put the required features into a new variety in the virtual certainty that they will appear without altering other (wanted) characteristics. Other methods have been tried over the years, with varying degrees of success, but the disadvantages have nearly always outweighed the benefits.

THE IMPORTANCE OF TASTE

'No fruit is more to our English taste than the apple. Let the Frenchman have his pear, the Italian his fig, the Jamaican may retain his farinaceous banana and the Malay his durian but for us, the apple.' This was said by Edward Bunyard, a notable English fruit nurseryman and connoisseur, in his excellent *Anatomy of Dessert* (1929).

Let's take this preference for the apple down to varietal level. An obvious example is the 'Golden Delicious' (which, interestingly, Bunyard himself introduced to England!). To some people, this dessert apple does not have enough flavour, but it is an American apple and most Americans prefer apples of this sort. The aromatic sweetness of the English Cox is not to their liking. Taste is very personal – what one individual thinks is delicious, another can strongly dislike – and it is impossible to describe the taste of a fruit without letting one's own feelings creep in.

However, what we *can* do is make sure we eat a fruit when it is at its best. The delicious French soft cheeses, if eaten when still hard, can taste a little soapy. Similarly, most unripe fruits have a turnip-like flavour. The apples sold and eaten in Great Britain, especially in supermarkets, are often well short of their best. At the point when 'Golden Delicious' is put on sale, it tastes foul. And 'McIntosh', 'Jonagold' and their derivatives are usually the same. It's a different story if they are allowed to ripen before being eaten, however. To remain in good condition throughout the period from picking to purchase, most fruits have to be picked well ahead of maturity. It is a real shame that shoppers aren't properly informed that the fruit they are buying is not yet ready to eat. Exactly the same goes for fruit grown at home: gardeners should find out what they are growing, and when it should be picked and eaten.

Eating a pear too early is even more of a crime than biting into an unripe apple. The crunch as it is being bitten into is alarming to hear, for in this condition it is barely better than a pear-shaped potato. A ripe pear is ready to eat when it yields a little when you press into it, and you should test it every day in this way until it does 'give' when pressed. Then there will be so much juice that it will practically have to be eaten in a bath. Incidentally, a pear picked too early will never ripen – it just goes rubbery.

THE WORLD OF FRUIT

We have looked at the way different fruits came into existence, where they came from, how they have been altered to be more attractive to us and how they have spread across the world over the centuries. Apart from looking at their future – which is always a hazardous occupation – all that really remains is to take a quick look at some of the more

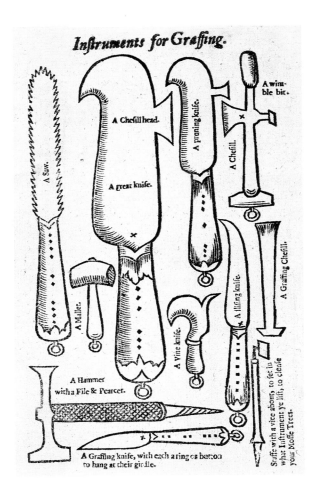
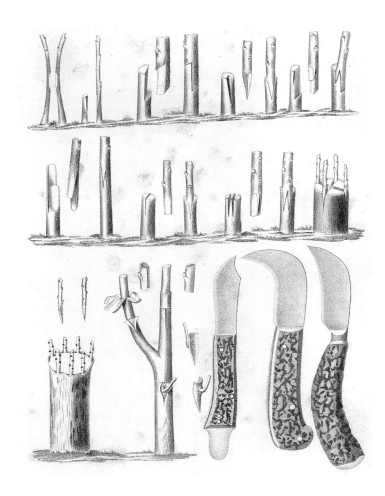

interesting statistics relating to their commercial production.

China is the world's largest apple-producing country, yielding a massive 20 million metric tonnes – and that is with only one main variety, 'Fuji'. (By comparison, the whole of Europe grows less than 16 million tonnes.) In second place is the USA, producing 6 million tonnes, a tenth of the world's apple production.

France tops the European apple, nectarine, peach and apricot lists, and produces 7 million tonnes of grapes. Italy is the dark horse of Europe, the second largest apple producer in Europe, and yields even vaster quantities of grapes than France (nearly 10 million tonnes). Germany manages to thrive by growing a lot of fruit that are less common in other countries. She comes third in the world apple stakes, for instance, but tops it in cherries and currants, and also heads the European strawberry list. Bearing in mind the country's substantial wine and sherry production, it comes as no great surprise that Spain is third in the European grape-growing list (after Italy and France), and shares the European citrus production honours with Italy (both somewhat aided by their largely Mediterranean climate). Spain is also the only country in Europe that produces bananas on any significant scale – half a million tonnes annually.

GRAFTING AND CUTTING TOOLS

ABOVE: Two illustrations showing the development of graftting and cutting tools. The first example (left) is from *The Countyman's New Art of Planting and Grafting* by Leonard Mascall, published in 1652; the example on the right comes from *Pomologie française*, by Pierre-Antoine Poiteau, published much later, in 1838.

1:Pome

The Alexander Apple.

The area of the Middle East known as the Fertile Crescent is popularly held to be the birthplace of human civilization, but it was also the cradle of many of today's commonly grown temperate-zone fruits. It is barely a surprise that the apple, which is the most popular and, widespread fruit, has played such an important part in folklore.

Greek myths abound with apple stories, and one of the best known must be that of Atalanta's race. Atalanta was a celebrated beauty, pursued by many good and true men. She was also an extremely accomplished runner, an ability that she used to sift the men from the boys amongst her plentiful suitors. It was a good system but not as sporting as it might sound, because if the young men lost the race (which they invariably did) they paid with their lives. This bloodthirsty routine continued until one day a young beau called Hippomenes appeared. He was determined to survive and win Atalanta, but he realized that without some guile he didn't stand a chance. Accordingly, he sought counselling from Venus (the goddess of love), who gave him three golden apples, and with these in his pocket he entered the race. As Atalanta passed him, Hippomenes threw one of the golden apples a little ahead of her so that she had to pause to pick it up. Three times this happened and three times he passed her, eventually winning both the race and Atalanta.

The theme of the golden apple crops up repeatedly in mythology. Even Hercules got entangled with them in the garden of the Hesperides while carrying out one of his famous labours. Zeus gave the garden to Hera as a wedding present upon their marriage. It was tended by three nymphs called the Hesperides and in its centre there grew a tree bearing golden apples. Hercules' task was to acquire some of these, but as well as having the nymphs to contend with there was a dragon wrapped round the base of the tree. In order to locate the garden, Hercules enlisted the aid of a minor sea god called Nereus, who had the useful power of metamorphosis. Hercules duly found the garden, along with its nymphs and dragon, but instead of turning him into stone (as was their wont) they permitted him to take a couple of the golden apples. However, once out of the garden, the apples began to tarnish. Hercules took them back immediately, whereupon they instantly regained their lustre.

The most famous example of apples in mythology is, of course, in the Bible, where (in the book of Genesis) they supposedly grew on the tree of the forbidden fruit. The interesting horticultural point about all these mythical trees is that 'apple' is often simply the word that translators have used to represent a fruit that was either unfamiliar to them

'ALEXANDER' (*MALUS DOMESTICA*)

OPPOSITE: Also known as 'Emperor Alexander', 'Alexander' is a very old variety (1700s), possibly Ukrainian, and arrived in England in 1817. This is an apple that looks a great deal better than it tastes, and is therefore a garden variety and one for the showbench. It ripens from September to November.

or likely to be so to their readers. Apples certainly grew in Mediterranean countries at that time but the pomegranate was far more common and its yellow-orange colour might easily be mistaken for gold. Maybe 'golden apples' were simply oranges or lemons – an interesting line of thought that could throw a great deal of mythology into question.

What we do know about apples and pears is that in temperate regions these two pome fruits are and always have been the tree fruits grown in the greatest quantity, both commercially and in gardens. All the genera and species in this group belong to the rose family, *Rosaceae*, and are characterized by having a core in which the seeds develop. The apple is the most widely grown, appearing in every country in the temperate zone as well as in many Mediterranean countries, and sometimes on higher ground in the Tropics. The importance of apples as a food cannot be overstated. They are eaten throughout the world and are extremely nourishing, as well as being good for the gums. Perfectly suited to today's bustling lifestyle, they are easy to grow and available anywhere, all year round.

With regards to wild varieties, the naturally occurring crab apples *Malus silvestris* and *M. pumila* are now scattered throughout the temperate region but almost certainly originated in the Caucasus and Turkestan. Wild apples in the Caucasus tend to be small and uneatable – what we think of as crab apples. However, many of those growing wild in Turkestan are much larger than the Caucasian fruits and equal to today's cultivars (varieties bred intentionally in cultivation). The complete range of sizes and qualities is found there. Natural hybridizing and mutating has occurred without intervention from humankind – a true case of nature at work and the survival of the fittest. This can also be seen in Russia, where the hardier Siberian crab, *Malus baccata*, has crossbred with other species and hybrids, producing extremely robust offspring that are able to tolerate the harsh winters. *M. baccata* also shows some resistance to the common fungus disease of apple scab, so its genes often appear deliberately in modern cultivars. This is the sort of thing that will be made possible by genetic modification (GM), where the time taken to produce disease-resistant cultivars could provide enormous benefits. Surely this is an excellent demonstration of the advantages of GM as opposed to the negative stories we encounter in the popular press and television.

During those very early times tribes were nomadic, but once they decided to settle in a particular place, apple trees and any other plants bearing superior qualities were retained when the ground was cleared for arable crops. However,

COLLECTION OF APPLES FROM LANGLEY'S *POMONA* (1729)
OPPOSITE: This is a selection of apples that were being grown in England during the first half of the eighteenth century. By modern standards, very few would be considered worth growing today – their size, quality, cropping and disease resistance would be unacceptable, but many are the ancestors of modern varieties.

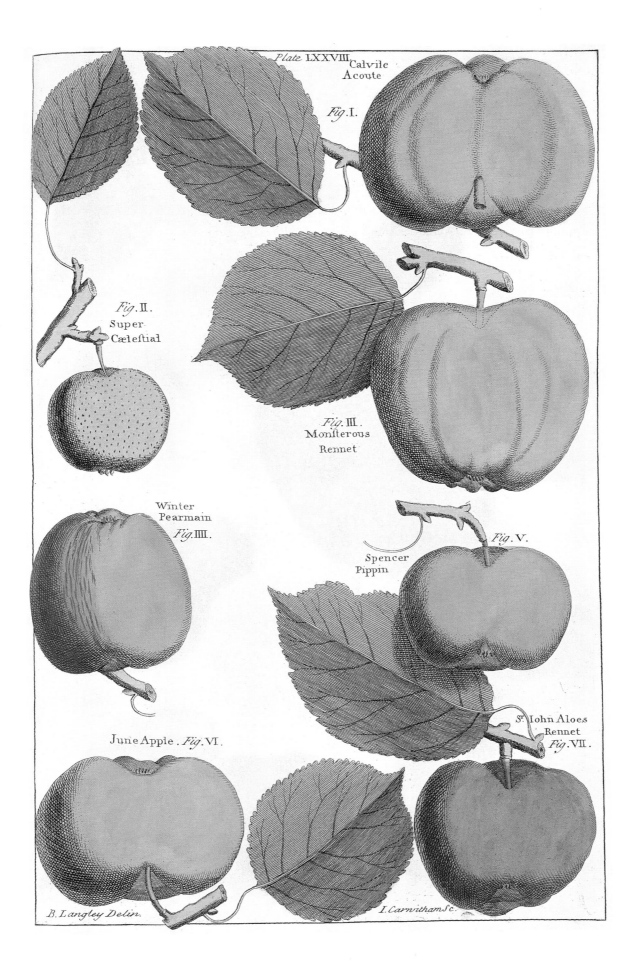

Plate LXXVIII. Calvile
Acoute

*Fig.*I.

*Fig.*II.
Super
Cælestial

*Fig.*III.
Monsterous
Rennet

Winter
Pearmain
*Fig.*IIII.

*Fig.*V.

Spencer
Pippin

Sʳ. Iohn Aloes
Rennet
*Fig.*VII.

June Apple. *Fig.*VI.

B. Langley Delin.

I. Carwitham Sc.

it wasn't merely superior fruits that could render trees worth keeping. They may have possessed other characteristics considered desirable in a food crop, such as pest or disease resistance, more compact growth or tolerance of drought. If the trees could not be saved, they would be grafted onto seedling rootstocks (sets of roots), growing in what were the forerunners of modern nurseries. This was human rather than natural selection, and constituted the beginning of commercial fruit growing and nursery work. The system of saving the best features gave rise to large gene pools of superior trees. Such selection, including rootstocks, is still in practice across the world and doubtless always will be. Just one outcome of those early experiments is thought to be *M. pumila*, giving rise to the range of 'Doucin' or 'Paradise' apple rootstocks, which are the forerunners of those we use today. Therefore we can say that the mechanism for spreading different kinds of fruit, and introducing new varieties and knowledge, developed in three main ways: from neighbouring countries, from the selection of wildings and through natural hybridizing.

Over the centuries fruit cultivation became more organized, developing in cultural centres such as monasteries. Gradually, varieties and cultivars were given names, whereas beforehand they had simply been 'apples'. In England, naming began as early as 1204, when we find the first mention of the 'Pearmain'. The 'Costard' and the 'Pippin' appeared soon afterwards. Although these are now considered generic names, they were regarded as actual varieties when first grown. Very little intentional hybridizing was performed and these early varieties were normally the result of natural crossbreeding aided by the skilful eyes of growers, who could spot improvements. The age of existing varieties and cultivars of apples varies enormously. 'Decio', which is in the National Fruit Collection at Brogdale in Kent, probably dates back to the time of the Roman invasion of Britain. By modern standards it is not of high quality, but it gives us a valuable insight into what was being grown long ago.

As we have seen, desirable characteristics in wild fruit trees were perpetuated by the practice of budding and grafting. In order to reproduce a fruit tree so that the new one is exactly the same as an existing one, vegetative propagation has to be implemented, which means budding, grafting or growing from cuttings. Hybrid trees of most kinds will not grow true from seed, even if raised from one of their own. Instead, they must be grown from a piece of shoot taken

COLLECTION OF APPLES FROM HUGH RONALDS' *PYRUS MALUS BRENTFORDIENIS* (*1831*)
OPPOSITE: 1. 'Early Wax', 2. 'Brown's Summer Beauty', 3. 'Thorll Pippin', 4. 'Sops of Wine', 5. 'Eve Apple', 6. 'Hicks' Fancy'. By the nineteenth century, the appearance of apples had changed for the better. Although 'Early Wax' still had the tall and turreted shape of much earlier apples, for example, the general trend was towards smoother and better-quality varieties. Breeding programmes and selection were largely responsible for this improvement.

Nº 1· Early Wax.
  2 Browns Summer Beauty.
  3· Thorll Pippin.

Nº 4· Sops of Wine.
  5· Eve Apple.
  6· Hicks' Fancy.

'CATSHEAD' (*MALUS DOMESTICA*)

ABOVE: Known in England in the 1600s and still grown today in private collections and gardens, this is a splendid example of an early cooking apple – large, deeply ribbed, frequently lop-sided and irregular. It remains, however, a high-quality and valuable October to January cooker whose crops become heavier with the age of the tree.

'KING OF THE PIPPINS' (*MALUS DOMESTICA*)

OPPOSITE: This fine, old dessert variety ripens from October to December, and will keep until March (although practically inedible). Its name and history are both rather confused. Thought to have originated in England, it is entangled with the French 'Reine des Reinettes'. Also listed as 'Golden Winter Pearmain' and 'King of the Pippins', it bears other aliases ('Hampshire Yellow' and 'Jones's Southampton Pippin').

from that tree, a characteristic that was noted as long ago as 332 BC by the Greek philosopher Theophrastus. This is still the way that varieties and cultivars of most woody plants, including fruit, are propagated today. One would think that taking cuttings would be the simplest and most productive method and, indeed, many bush fruits are propagated by this method. However, cuttings of most pome fruits do not root easily, so they must be budded or grafted. When grafting, a short length of young shoot (the 'scion') is inserted under the bark of a growing set of roots (the 'rootstock'). The area of the union is bound with raffia or plastic tape, and is then waxed. This protection is left in place until buds on the scion start to grow, and it is this new growth that makes the new tree. Budding is a faster and more economical way to propagate, as just a single growth bud is used instead of a length of shoot. Despite the fact that fruit trees had been raised in this way for over two thousand years, it was really only in the last century that any serious work was carried out to simplify and reduce the huge number of existing rootstocks, principally amongst apples. This involved setting up trials for rootstocks from all over the world. Hence, some years after its birth in 1913, what was then known as the East Malling Research Station in Kent produced a shortlist of recommended rootstocks for all kinds of different tree fruit. Since this time, classified rootstocks, fruiting varieties and cultivars have all been propagated vegetatively.

In the USA, the pattern of development in the progress and management of cultivated fruit was (on the whole) similar to that in Britain. Of course, there were specific research projects pertaining to local conditions, but in those early years of the country the establishment of food sources was probably more important than the esoteric side of fruit growing. One man who might be said to have cocked a snook at both tradition and science was John Chapman, better known by his nickname of Johnny Appleseed. Chapman was born in Leominster, Massachusetts in 1774 and the story goes that he travelled the country with a satchel slung over his shoulder, scattering apple seeds wherever the spirit willed him. Although appealing, the story does him little credit, as he would certainly have known that apples grown from seed never come true to type. What he actually did was establish a string of apple nurseries from Pennsylvania in the east, through Ohio and west into Indiana. He carried this out with great success from about 1800 until his death in 1845, by which time New England had a thriving fruit export business, sending apples as far afield as the West Indies. Chapman was definitely a colourful character but, contrary to popular belief, he was not the father of

'RIBSTON PIPPIN' (*MALUS DOMESTICA*)

OPPOSITE: 'Ribston Pippin' is one of the best known and most famous of the older generation of eating apples. It probably came from a pip out of an apple growing in Rouen (northern France) towards the end of the seventeenth century. Along with others, this was planted at Little Ribston Hall near Knaresborough, Yorkshire. 'Cox's Orange Pippin' is one of its many children.

commercial fruit growing in the USA. He did an enormous amount to build up orcharding in the east, but the centre of the apple industry lay on the other side of the continent, in the north-western state of Washington. Nor did Simpson produce the first commercial apple variety in the USA. That was almost certainly one of those brought from England. It is possible that the first domestically bred, commercial American apple came in 1824, from Fort Vancouver in Washington State. Rather romantically, it was one of a batch of seedlings raised by a certain Captain Simpson, from the pips of an apple he had eaten at his farewell dinner party in England. What a shame nobody took the trouble to find out (or remember) its name.

In fact, it was Henderson Luelling and William Meek from Iowa who were responsible for the initial growth of the apple industry in the USA. Along with other fortune seekers, Luelling set off west in his covered wagon. Rather strangely, this wagon was full of soil and apple trees, which presumably resulted in more than a few raised eyebrows. This was not the only effect, as the whole rig was so immensely heavy that he soon lost sight of the other travellers. Fortunately, some Native Americans who encountered Luelling came to the conclusion that he was a penniless and harmless eccentric. Upon reaching Washington State (no mean feat in itself), Luelling met up with William Meek and together they began planting orchards. This was a particularly opportune time and place for such a venture, as the West was gradually being brought under control and gold prospectors were both thick on the ground and hungry. By the time local demand began to wane, a railway stretched from the Atlantic to the Pacific, and fruit could be moved anywhere it was required. Washington State rapidly became the largest apple-producing area in the world.

Other things were happening in America at the same time. There is a plaque commemorating an apple, in a field near Lake Michigan, Iowa. In the mid-nineteenth century a farmer called Jesse Hiatt noticed a sucker growing from the rootstock of a tree. This is not an uncommon occurrence even today, but instead of being pulled up this particular sucker was allowed to grow into a tree. When the tree fruited, the apples were bright red with an excellent flavour and aroma. Hiatt named the variety 'Hawkeye' and sent some to a friend of his who was a judge. The judge described them as 'Delicious, delicious.' In 1895, Stark Bros, the famous American nursery, released the variety as 'Delicious' and thus began a story that continues today. It soon became the most popular commercial apple in the apple-growing world, and

'POMME DE FINALE' (*MALUS DOMESTICA*)

OPPOSITE: Here we have an apple variety that appears to exist in many different forms and variations. With modern knowledge, we can say it is far more likely to have been originally grown from pips and that each tree of the so-called 'new' variety had its own characteristics. The same effect can be achieved today, if several pips from an apple core are sown. Each resulting tree will be different and individual.

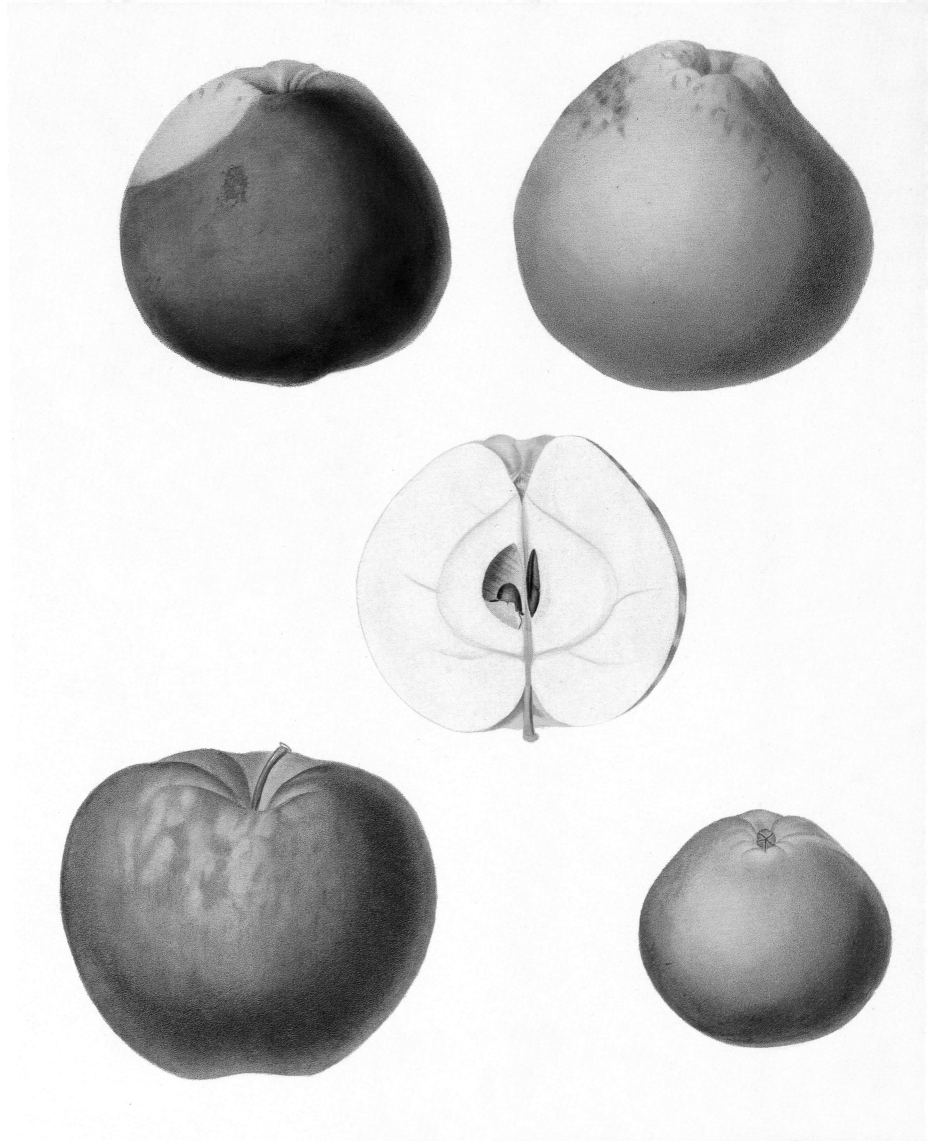

The Red Quarenden Apple.

by the mid-1920s it was estimated that there were between seven and eight million trees. Several sports (naturally occurring variations) have mutated from 'Delicious', the best known probably being 'Red Delicious'. Oddly, 'Golden Delicious' has no connection with 'Delicious'. It was a chance seedling found in West Virginia in 1890 and released onto the market in 1914, again by Stark Bros.

One interesting thing about apples – and other plants, both fruit and ornamental – is that subtle differences crop up from time to time. These are often not big enough to warrant the description of 'sport' or 'mutant' but are significant enough to catch the nurseryman's eye. It could be that one tree ripens a few days earlier than the rest or that it exhibits better disease resistance. Any small change viewed as an improvement by the nurseryman could lead to the favouring of a particular tree the next time a batch of new trees is propagated, for it might even be easier to propagate. This is an ongoing exercise and means that when we look at a bowl of apples today the fruit is not necessarily exactly as it would have been a hundred years ago. It is for this very reason that we have National Collections, such as the one at Brogdale devoted to fruit. At these institutions, existing trees are used as mother trees for their own replacement to prevent the introduction of different 'blood' into the collections.

Apples were not the only fruit to originate in Central Asia, however. A great many others that are today regarded as everyday food in the temperate regions also started life in Central Asia. This is not as odd as it seems, because way back at the dawn of plant life most plants were developing from a common ancestor. Their appearance can only be guessed at or sometimes learned from fossils. Botanically, all the fruit plants we are familiar with today probably looked very similar. The similarities were such that, until comparatively recent times, they were classified in the same botanical family, the *Rosaceae*. Over millions of years, evolution has caused them to become less alike, but their origins remain the same.

The pear is the apple's closest relative (particularly in appearance), and also began life in the Fertile Crescent. The central species was almost certainly *Pyrus communis,* but there were many other species that crossed with it. Like apples, so much natural hybridizing occurred that the starting point is now somewhat blurred. It must not be forgotten that the different species of fruit spread eastwards into China and Japan as well as into Europe. Those now grown in the Far

'RED QUARRENDEN' (*MALUS DOMESTICA*)
OPPOSITE: This would have been the original name for 'Devonshire Quarrenden'. Although it clearly has strong connections with Devon, 'Red Quarrenden' probably originated in Normandy, the word 'quarrenden' possibly being a corruption of 'Carentan' in Normandy. The earliest record of it is in 1690 and, during the eighteenth century it became a much-prized and excellent early (August/September) eating apple throughout Great Britain.

'WELLINGTON' (*MALUS DOMESTICA*)

ABOVE: Christened 'Dumelow's Seedling', this is a high-quality cooking variety. The 'Wellington' is an excellent apple, but its gorgeous pink blossom is an equally great virtue. It was raised by a Leicestershire farmer some time late in the eighteenth century – this we know because the original tree was standing and healthy in 1800. It was renamed 'Wellington' in 1819 or 1820, presumably after the famous English duke.

COLLECTION OF APPLES FROM HUGH RONALDS' *PYRUS MALUS BRENTFORDIENIS* (*1831*)

OPPOSITE: 1. 'Striped June Eating', 2. 'Summer Oslin', 3. 'Kerry Pippin', 4. 'Summer Pippin', 5. 'Tartarian Crab', 6. 'Duchess of Oldenburgh'. This group of apples contains one of particular interest, the 'Summer Oslin' (more correctly just 'Oslin', or the 'Burr Knot'). This is one of a very few apple varieties that can be propagated from cuttings, which would be taken in early winter. Although it is of good quality, there are plenty better apples, so its curious ability to root readily is probably the main reason it is grown.

1. Striped Juneating
2. Summer Oslin
3. Kerry Pippin.
4. Summer Pippin
5. Tartarian Crab.
6. Duchefs of Oldenburgh.

Pomme de Montalivet.

East are more likely to be descended from *P. serotina*, the 'Chinese Sand Pear'. It is unlikely that *P. communis* was ever gathered and eaten straight from the wild, as it was far too small, hard and gritty to be appetizing, even to early man. It has to be assumed that natural hybridizing, and the survival of the fittest, led to fruits that were considered pleasant to eat. As with apples, it is most probable that the deliberate cultivation of pears originated in southern Russia, from where the varieties spread into the Fertile Crescent and then to Greece, Italy and Western Europe. We know that they were grown in Italy two thousand years ago because wall paintings in the remains of Pompeii (which was destroyed in AD 79) show them to be just as plump and attractive as they are today. It is not certain when pear cultivation started in Britain, but it seems likely that the Romans brought them, since they were so popular in their homeland. We do know that they were growing at the time of the Norman Conquest in 1066 because the Domesday Book (1086) mentions the use of very old pear trees as boundary markers in what is now Gloucestershire. It is also clear that early in the ninth century several different varieties were in cultivation in France. Knowing the exchange of material and information that took place between monasteries, it is unimaginable that they did not reach Britain.

Around the eleventh century, it was discovered that, where fruit quality was concerned, not all pear rootstocks give equally good results. For example, when wild pear seedlings were used as rootstocks, the results were inferior to those from trees grown on rootstocks raised from cultivated pears. Even today, when quince rootstocks are used, it is recognized that a modern pear cultivar grown on a seedling pear rootstock is different in several respects from the same cultivar grown on a quince rootstock. There are also differences when the same cultivar is grafted onto an existing pear tree of another cultivar. The liaison between pears and their quince rootstocks is further complicated, for some cultivars of pear are incompatible with quince (notably 'Williams'). This means that an interstock of another pear variety is inserted between the 'Williams' bud and the quince rootstock when budding or grafting.

Also from around the eleventh century, France was establishing itself as the pear centre of Europe. The varieties grown in Britain up to the fourteenth century were all of French origin and it was not until late in that century that

---

'POMME DE MONTALIVET' (*MALUS DOMESTICA*)

OPPOSITE: It is not uncommon in older books about plants for the author or artist to include their favourite varieties, regardless of whether they are known by or available to anyone else. 'Pomme de Montalivet' has all the hallmarks of one of these varieties. It is a good-looking apple, but one that appears in no books other than the one carrying its portrait, Poiteau's *Pomologie française*. Here it is said to be of US origin, introduced to France under the Empire, by Comte Lelieur of Ville-sur-Arce, who became administrator of the royal gardens. Its only merit seems to be its size.

the first English cultivar appeared, called the 'Wardon' or 'Worden'. It was a baking pear, as were most cultivars and varieties of the time. Only from the mid-sixteenth century do we find mention of juicy (dessert) pears. The manner in which cultivars passed from one country to another also began to change. Instead of whole trees making the journey, nurserymen, growers and gardeners were more likely to send young winter shoots for grafting onto rootstocks in the spring. For short distances, they probably sent summer shoots for budding. This was particularly useful to the English nobility, because any garden of note had to have French pears growing in it; therefore we find pears with clearly English names (such as 'Early Katherine', the 'Norwich', 'Worcester' and 'Long Green') growing alongside French cultivars like 'Beurré du Roy', 'Bon Chrétien' and 'Montpelier'.

Although France was the centre of pear cultivation in sixteenth- and seventeenth-century Europe, much of the breeding work took place in Belgium. 'Glou Morceau' started life in Mons in 1750 and remains an excellent dessert pear. Despite its French name, 'Williams' Bon Chrétien' is English in origin. It is not known how the name came about, but it is possibly an early example of perception carrying more weight than fact – give it a foreign name and it will sell like hot cakes. Anyway, 'Williams' first appeared in 1770 and, twenty years later, it made its way to North America. Several years later again, it was found by Enoch Bartlett, who was unaware of its name and so gave it his own. 'Bartlett' soon became the 'Delicious' of the pear world and now dominates the pear-canning business. 'Doyenné du Comice' is probably the best dessert pear and first fruited in 1849 at Angers, France. Within a few years it was being grown throughout Europe and the USA. Along with apples, pears are now grown throughout the world, wherever the climate and soil are suitable. Generally, dessert cultivars do not grow as well as apples in more northerly regions, as they need a longer and warmer summer to ripen to perfection. Given the protection of a sunny wall, they will normally succeed. To many, however, France still breeds and grows the best pears in the world.

Although the pear is visually the closest relative of the apple, its next of kin is actually the quince. Structurally they are very similar, and nowadays all pear trees are grown on quince rootstocks, while apples will only grow on apple rootstocks. The quince that is grown for its fruit is called *Cydonia oblonga*. This has much the same origin as the apple and the pear, in that it is found growing wild in Central Asia. However, there is no such thing as a dessert quince amongst

'POMME DE ROSEE' (*MALUS DOMESTICA*)

OPPOSITE: This apple seems to have vanished off the face of the earth, leaving only its name and portrait behind. The National Apple Register of the United Kingdom, which includes many overseas varieties, fails to recognize it, and so do French fruit books, old and new (though Poiteau says it was grown in Calvados). It tastes best between late August and mid-September, though can be kept until October.

modern cultivars. They must be cooked thoroughly, as they are too hard to eat *au naturel*. (Strangely, the ornamental quince, which has smaller fruits, belongs to the genus *Chaenomeles*.) Due to its rather chilly place of origin, the cultivated quince is extremely hardy but requires a longer and hotter summer than is usual in northern temperate-region countries. Although Central Asia has bitterly cold winters, the summers are generally long and hot, so a Mediterranean climate is perfect. This is borne out by its popularity and commercial cultivation in Greece, Italy, Spain and the Middle East, where the quince is highly valued. In cooler regions, the cultivar 'Vranja' is usually the most successful. The quince was grown quite widely in England from medieval times until the sixteenth and seventeenth centuries, when it was used for quince marmalade, jelly and a cooked dessert similar to Spain's modern *membrillo*. One virtue, or perhaps it is a vice, is the strong, sweet scent emitted by ripe quinces. In the past, this served as an effective air freshener and, presumably with the same purpose in mind, the Mesopotamians would use quinces to sweeten the atmosphere in their desert tents. All this makes the quince a very pleasant and desirable fruit, but it is not in the same league as the apple or pear. The quince is something of a Cinderella among fruits.

As with all the fruits in this chapter, the medlar, *Mespilus germanica*, is another member of the *Rosaceae* family and a product of Central Asia. From there it spread to Persia and Europe, and then crossed the Atlantic with settlers to North America – today it is so at home in the USA that it is even grown as a handsome hedging plant in the south. As is often the case, it has been found growing wild in mainland Europe, North America and even in southern England, though these last specimens would have spread from the captivity of a garden. Nevertheless, the medlar is considered a perfectly legitimate garden plant, although opinions differ regarding its value as an eating fruit. The medlar is closely related to the hawthorn and you can see this quite clearly by looking at the fruits, which are simply giant hawthorn berries. The two most commonly grown cultivars are the 'Dutch' and the 'Nottingham', both of which could date back to Roman times. It is hardly surprising that the medlar is grown as much for its attractive, large, white flowers as for its odd, large brown fruits (which are not fit for eating until almost completely rotten).

In England, medlars were commonly used to treat upset stomachs during the Middle Ages. Today's opinion would seem to be somewhat at odds with this, as medlars are noted for their occasionally violent laxative properties.

'FLOWER OF KENT' (*MALUS DOMESTICA*)

OPPOSITE: This must be one of the most famous apples ever to have existed. It is the type that fell on Sir Isaac Newton and led to the creation of the laws of gravity. Although 'Flower of Kent' is its original and preferred name, history has led to it being referred to on more than one occasion as 'Sir Isaac Newton's Apple'.

'CARLISLE CODLING' (*MALUS DOMESTICA*)

ABOVE: The 'Carlisle Codling' is almost a relic of the original codlin cooking apples, for it is rather small, green, irregular and angular. Maybe it is not a thing of beauty, but this still a high-quality apple, in use from August to December. Its ability to be fit for use long before maturity explains such a long season.

'ROBINSON'S PIPPIN' (*MALUS DOMESTICA*)

OPPOSITE: This is a smallish dessert apple, tasting a little like 'Golden Pippin' and 'Nonpareil'. The small fruit size is often blamed on its habit of carrying the fruit in clusters of eight to ten towards the end of the branches. It is said to have been raised by the publican Robinson, of the Packhorse Inn, Turnham Green, London, dating back at least as far as 1816 when it was painted (by William Hooker). Although it is small apple, looking more like a crab apple, in its heyday 'Robinson's Pippin' was judged to be of excellent quality.

'API ETOILE' (*MALUS DOMESTICA*)

ABOVE: The 'Api Etoile' (also called 'Api Etoillé') proves that apples come in all shapes and sizes, though its curiosity value is considerably greater than all its other aspects added together. Peculiarity has its attractions, however, and this flat, star-shaped French apple is most certainly rather different.

'CALVILLE BLANC' (*MALUS DOMESTICA*)

OPPOSITE: Also called 'Calville Blanc d'Hiver' or 'Calville Blanche', this is one of the most famous varieties of all time and also one of the oldest, being recorded as long ago as 1598. Its true origin is unknown, but it is thought to be either French or German. It is still grown today in the *Potager du Roi* (King's Kitchen Garden) at Versailles.

'LEMON PIPPIN' (*MALUS DOMESTICA*)

ABOVE: This very old cooking apple probably dates back to the seventeenth century (when it was frequently sliced and dried). When mature, the characteristic shape and colour of the 'Lemon Pippin' are so lemon-like that it has been regularly mistaken for one (medium-sized and oval, its stalk is often covered by a fleshy protuberance). It makes a passable dessert apple late in its season (from autumn to spring), though it is very seldom grown nowadays. The tree (though not large) is very hardy, and is a good cropper.

'REINETTE JAUNE HATIVE' (*MALUS DOMESTICA*)

OPPOSITE: The 'Reinette Jaune Hâtive' is a very old French variety, possibly going back as far as 1628. The names of very old varieties are really more descriptions than labels – *reinette* barely has a meaning, like the English 'pippin'; *jaune* is the French for 'yellow'; and *hâtive* means 'early'. So this is an early-ripening, yellow apple.

'COCKLE'S PIPPIN' (*MALUS DOMESTICA*)

ABOVE: This apple was raised in about 1800 by someone called Cockle in Sussex, England. Though it is very similar to, and often confused with, 'Nutmeg Pippin', they are different varieties. It is an unremarkable, late eating apple and the fruit is medium-sized and conical. Older varieties are often conical, but the shape went out of fashion, although it seems to be reappearing lately. The flesh is crisp, yellow and has a pleasing flavour, but it does need a warm summer.

'GRAVENSTEIN' (*MALUS DOMESTICA*)

OPPOSITE: The 'Gravenstein' tastes far better than it looks. It is a very old Continental variety, reaching England via Denmark, where it arrived in about 1669. It was said to have originated in the garden of the Duke of Augustenberg, at the Castle of Graefenstein in Schleswig-Holstein (Germany), but others say it was an apple called 'Ville Blanc', which came from Italy and was only later taken to the Castle of Graefenstein.

'REDSTREAK' (*MALUS DOMESTICA*)

ABOVE: In the seventeenth century, when it first appeared, the 'Redstreak' was one of the most popular apples, and was also considered the best cider apple in Herefordshire. But its popularity didn't appear to last, because we find Nourse saying that, in spite of it being 'highly esteemed for its noble colour and smell; 'tis likewise fat and oily in the taste'.

'COX'S ORANGE PIPPIN' (*MALUS DOMESTICA*)

RIGHT: Many people consider this to be the finest of all eating apples, with near-perfect proportions of sweetness, acidity and aroma, but it is not an easy apple to grow. Susceptible to a wide range of pests and diseases – and all too often picked and eaten before its best – it is far better left to the professional fruit grower.

2. Cox's Orange Pippin.

'EMBROIDERED PIPPIN' (*MALUS DOMESTICA*)

ABOVE: The 'Embroidered Pippin' is the very opposite to 'Gravenstein', in that it looks a good deal better than it tastes. This is a poor-quality, winter eating apple. It is similar to the French 'Fenouillet Jaune' and was first recorded in 1806.

'BLENHEIM ORANGE' (*MALUS DOMESTICA*)

OPPOSITE: This wild seedling was found in around 1740, near Blenheim, Oxfordshire. Any pollen that its flowers produce is sterile, so it is useless as a pollinating variety. It also makes a very large tree if on the wrong rootstock. It was a popular dual-purpose apple, but modern varieties have superseded it commercially and the tree is too big for most modern gardens.

'FOXWHELP' (*MALUS DOMESTICA*)

ABOVE: This very famous Herefordshire cider apple dates back well into the seventeenth century and is still grown today. The only real difference between cider, cooking and eating apples is in their chemical make-up (the three most important elements of which are acidity, sweetness and aromatic status), which explains why different varieties have different uses.

'PIGEONNET DE ROUEN' (*MALUS DOMESTICA*)

LEFT: Along with 'Reinette' and 'Calville', 'Pigeon', 'Pigeonnet' and 'Pigeonette' are all used to describe French apples, being the equivalent of the British 'Pippin' and 'Codlin'. The 'Pigeonnet de Rouen' is an old variety, probably originating in Normandy, which dates from about 1755. It is an early dessert apple (although of second-rate quality) but does have an attractive appearance.

'SIBERIAN HARVEY CRAB' (*MALUS DOMESTICA*)

ABOVE: This apple is the result of a cross made early in the 1800s by Thomas Andrew Knight, between a 'Yellow Siberian' crab and a 'Golden Harvey'. It is one of the most widely used cider apples, and is used for its intensely sweet juice (which leads to a cider with a high alcohol content).

'RED AUGUST SIBERIAN CRAB' (*MALUS DOMESTICA*)

OPPOSITE: This is definitely grown for its ornamental value, rather than for the economic value of its fruit (which are very small and, from a distance, look more like cherries than apples, with a stalk as long as the fruit). The ground colour is a lovely primrose yellow, and almost completely covered with bright red on the sunny side. The 'Red August Siberian Crab' makes an excellent specimen tree for an ornamental garden.

'NORFOLK BEEFING' (*MALUS DOMESTICA*)

ABOVE: This apple has many aliases – twenty-nine, according to the National Apple Register. One of them, 'Norfolk Beaufin', suggests a French connection, but this is not so: it is a pure-bred Norfolk variety and the 'beefing' refers to its visual resemblance to roast beef when it is baked. It was first recorded in 1807, and is a very late, excellent cooker, staying usable (when well stored) until June.

'SCARLET PEARMAIN' (*MALUS DOMESTICA*)

OPPOSITE: Once known as 'Bell's Scarlet', this started life sometime before 1800. Unusually, it shares this name with three other quite distinct varieties of 'Scarlet Pearmain'. Although mix-ups can sometimes occur, this variety is considerably better known (and a better apple) than the others, so confusion is minimal.

Api Noir.

De l'Imprimerie de Langlois

'API NOIR' (*MALUS DOMESTICA*)

ABOVE: A rather nice story (though it cannot be proved) says that the original 'Api' variety was brought from the Peloponnese to Rome by Appius Claudius. 'Api Noir' is very similar to the original, but is dark crimson – almost black – and very shiny when polished. It is not as good as 'Api', and only grown as a curiosity.

'POMME VIOLET' (*MALUS DOMESTICA*)

OPPOSITE: The only record of this apple, besides this portrait in Hooker's *Fruits* (1818), was when it was exhibited in 1883 as a late-fruiting variety. Another apple going under the same name is 'Calville Rouge d'Automne Violette'.

'CARDINALE' (*PYRUS COMMUNIS*)

ABOVE: 'Cardinale's colour was its main attribute, which we can deduce from the fact that writers and gardeners give it only scant attention. However, varieties of this sort still have a part to play in large gardens, because (like crab apples amongst apple trees) they are often good pollinators for the fruiting varieties and certainly add colour and interest. They also provide excellent food for birds and humans alike.

'CHAUMONTELLE' (*PYRUS COMMUNIS*)

OPPOSITE: This was found as a wild seedling near Chantilly (north of Paris) as long ago as 1660. The original tree perished in 1789 (coincidentally, the same year as the French Revolution), due to a particularly hard winter. Its very uneven surface covers a high-quality flesh, though the fruit is inclined to be gritty.

The Chaumontelle Pear

'ANGELIQUE DE BORDEAUX' (*PYRUS COMMUNIS*)

ABOVE: Formerly known as 'Angelica', this French pear is thought to have reached England in about 1708, by way of the famous nurseryman George London. It was grown for about a century as 'St Martial', which some believe to be its original name.

'LITTLE MUSCAT' (*PYRUS COMMUNIS*)

LEFT: Although there are several varieties that carry the word 'Muscat' in their name, there does not seem to be a 'Little Muscat' amongst them. In fact, it is hard to imagine what size it can have been, because all 'Muscat' varieties are described as small. Its uncommonly small size could possibly account for its disappearance.

PEAR VARIETIES FROM HOGG'S *HEREFORDSHIRE POMONA* (1876–85)
BELOW: 'Forelle', 'Louise Bonne of Jersey', 'Williams' Bon Chrétien', 'Beurre d'Amanlis' and 'Flemish Beauty'. Of these five pears, at least three are still widely grown. 'Louise Bonne of Jersey' dates back to 1788 and was originally called just 'Louise'. This was then extended to 'Louise Bonne', and later to 'Louise Bonne d'Avranches', then finally was given its present name. 'Williams' Bon Chrétien' ('Bartlett') is described later (on page 69). 'Beurré d'Amanlis' is of uncertain origin, but used to be widely grown, and these days there are many better varieties.

'CHÊNE-VERT' (*PYRUS COMMUNIS*)
OPPOSITE: Any pear that has earned the name of 'Chêne-Vert' ('Evergreen Oak') certainly deserves a place in this book. However, it does pose more questions about the variety than it answers, and unfortunately there is no mention of it anywhere other than its naming in Pierre-Antoine Poiteau's *Pomologie française*, from which this illustration is taken.

'JARGONELLE' (*PYRUS COMMUNIS*)

ABOVE: Like many great pears, 'Jargonelle' is very old, and French in origin. It is extremely hardy, even in Scotland (where cooler summers prevail) and needs the protection of a sunny wall where it will succeed admirably. In appearance, it is not unlike 'Conference' – quite long and narrow, and green with variable patches of russet. It ripens in the second half of August and has to be picked at just the right time, as it has an unfortunate tendency to go brown from the centre outwards.

'BON CHRETIEN D'ETE' (*PYRUS COMMUNIS*)

OPPOSITE: Although not listed among its synonyms, this pear is more commonly known in the UK as 'Summer Bon Chrétien'. It is an inferior variety – the tree is rather tender and the fruit has a 'pleasant flavour' (which is a polite way of suggesting it is rather watery) – though it does cook quite well.

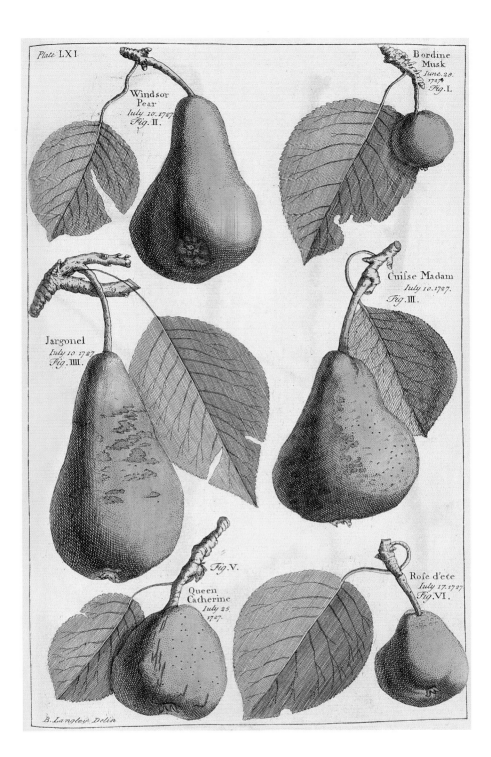

PEAR VARIETIES FROM LANGLEY'S *POMONA* (1729)

ABOVE: 'Windsor Pear', 'Bordine Musk', 'Jargonel', 'Cuisse Madam', 'Queen Catherine', 'Rose d'Eté' − a selection of pears grown in England in the first half of the eighteenth century. The standard of pears was not as high as for apples − few English-bred varieties were available and most French ones needed better summers than England could provide.

'BARTLETT' (*PYRUS COMMUNIS*)

OPPOSITE: Formerly 'Williams Bon Chrétien', it is unclear who actually bred this world-famous variety, but we do know that it first appeared at Aldermaston, Berkshire, shortly before 1770. The nurseryman who propagated and distributed it was Mr Williams of Turnham Green, Middlesex. Then, upon reaching America in 1799 (through a Mr Bartlett, near Boston), it entered a period of quiescence, and was renamed after its new owner. 'Bartlett' has since become the most widely grown pear in the world.

'UNNAMED PEAR' (*Pyrus communis*)

ABOVE: Despite its good looks, resembling both 'Beurré Hardy' and 'Comice', it is unthinkable that an artist of the calibre and knowledge of William Hooker would be ignorant of its name. Therefore, it is almost certain that this pear has no name rather than one that has been forgotten.

BEURRE D'ARENBURG (*Pyrus communis*)

OPPOSITE: This variety is often confused with the very similar-looking 'Glou Morceau', though they are distinct from one another. The only way out of any confusion is to settle for the variety that is most likely, or the one that occurs most frequently. This is a good dessert pear – though not an outstanding one – whose main virtue is its late ripening.

'DOYENNE DU COMICE' (*PYRUS COMMUNIS*)

ABOVE: 'Comice' is unquestionably the finest pear in the world. It is large and at its impeccable best in November. The mouth-watering flesh is pale yellow, most deliciously flavoured and juicy to the point of indecency. Following its conception and birth, some time before its first fruiting in 1849 (in Angers, France), it was brought to England by Sir Thomas Dyke Acland in 1858.

'VERTE LONGUE PANACHEE' (*PYRUS COMMUNIS*)

OPPOSITE: This variety's main claim to fame is the curiosity value of its genuinely striped fruit, leaves and (sometimes) young shoots. It has all the appearances of a 'chimera sport' – this occurs when, following budding or grafting, some cells of the rootstock actually enter the scion variety and exist in a separate layer. The different characteristics of the variety and the rootstock may then appear individually rather than mixed.

'CRASANNE' (*PYRUS COMMUNIS*)

BELOW: France has always dominated the pear scene and, in qualitative terms at least, she continues to do so. This very old variety has only been replaced by modern ones because its size and shape do not fit in with the modern image of a saleable fruit. However, it is still a fine dessert pear, dating back to at least 1693.

CHINESE SAND PEAR (*PYRUS PYRIFOLIA*)

RIGHT: This is a hybrid of two other species (*P. serotina* and *P. sinensis*) which until the 1980s were virtually unknown outside the Far East, where three thousand varieties existed. They reached the United States in the gold rush days, when Chinese labourers brought seeds with them. They are now widely cultivated in Australasia, the western United States, Central America and southern Europe. Their flavour is weaker than European pears and the oldest varieties had a very gritty flesh, a facet that has since been bred out. 'Hosui', 'Kosui', 'Nijisseiki', 'Shinseiki', 'Nashi' and 'Shinsui' are the most popular varieties.

沙梨

'ELTON' (*PYRUS COMMUNIS*)

ABOVE: This excellent English seedling pear was discovered in 1812 by Thomas Andrew Knight, growing at Elton in Herefordshire. Even at that time, Knight estimated its age as being about 170 years, which is an exceptionally long time for it to have been standing there without being noticed.

'MARTIN SEC' (*PYRUS COMMUNIS*)

OPPOSITE: This is undoubtedly one of the earliest recorded cultivated pears (if not *the* earliest) and is thus of real interest. It is mentioned as being the pear (among other fruits) that was delivered to the Treasury by King Edward I's fruiterer in 1292. Though it was described at the time as a dessert variety, remember that the parameters were completely different then, and by today's standards would be considered more as a cooker. It is also recommended by Jean-Baptiste de la Quintinye in the late seventeenth century and William Forsyth in the early nineteenth.

Martin Sec.

'SECKLE' (*PYRUS COMMUNIS*)

OPPOSITE: This small, high-quality American pear was found
in a wood near Philadelphia by a trapper called Dutch Jacob.
Considered by William Coxe, the American horticulturist, to be
the best pear 'of this or any other country' (which is
understandable, since he died before 'Comice' appeared),
'Seckle' was a seedling from a discarded pear core. It took its
name from a later owner of the land on which it originally grew.

'SANGUINOLE' (*PYRUS COMMUNIS*)

ABOVE: This is more a curio than a serious variety, and is
extremely old. Its bright-red flesh is striking, but this does seem
to be its only real claim to fame. It might well be the same
variety as the 'Blood Red Pear' mentioned by Parkinson in his
Paradisi in Sole, Paradisus Terrestris (1629).

QUINCE (*CYDONIA OBLONGA*)

LEFT AND OPPOSITE: The quince has never been cultivated widely in the cooler parts of the world, for it is much happier in a Mediterranean climate. It goes back so far that its true origin is not known for certain, though everything points towards its coming from the traditional birthplace of most pome fruits – Turkestan and the Caucasus – where it still grows wild. Mesopotamia also featured in the quince's early history as one of the first countries to cultivate it. The quince soon spread south to the Mediterranean and, by the time Pliny was writing (in the first century AD), there were large areas of cultivated quince in Crete.

QUINCE (*CYDONIA OBLONGA*)

ABOVE: The genera *Cydonia*, *Pyrus* and *Chaenomele*s have been inextricably entangled for hundreds of years, so it is not very likely that the position will be resolved easily. The present situation is this: *Cydonia* represents the cultivated quinces, *Pyrus* covers pears, and *Chaenomeles* stands for the ornamental quinces (including what many of us call japonica).

'PORTUGAL' (*CYDONIA OBLONGA*)

OPPOSITE: Probably the highest-quality variety, this is strongly recommended for cooking and preserving. It takes longer than other varieties to come into bearing and does best in warmer climates.

'PEAR-SHAPED QUINCE' (*Cydonia oblonga*)

ABOVE: This name, though seemingly strange, distinguishes it adequately from other quince varieties (there is even an 'Apple-Shaped' one). The 'Pear-Shaped Quince' was one of several old varieties described by Parkinson in 1629, though it was not rated as being particularly good, due to its rather dry flesh.

QUINCE (*Cydonia oblonga*)

OPPOSITE: The modern quince is a very different fruit to the ancient variety pictured here. Several varieties are grown, all of which are larger and of better quality than the originals. 'Vranja', indistin-guishable from 'Bereczki', is the main variety for gardens, but 'Pear-Shaped' and 'Portugal' also have a considerable following.

MEDLAR (MESPILUS GERMANICA)
ABOVE: The medlar has attracted more than its fair share of indelicate and uncomplimentary names, and most countries that grow the fruit give it their own colloquial names. Some people say that it tastes as bad as it looks. Although it is an acquired taste, those who have discovered its hidden pleasures stand by it staunchly. It has to be allowed to ripen on the tree, however.

MEDLARS AND QUINCES FROM LANGLEY'S POMONA (1729)
OPPOSITE: 1. Medlar, 2. Pear-quince 'Portugal', 3. Apple-quince 'Portugal', 4. Service, 5. English Quince, 6. Berberry. The medlar was popular in England during the Middle Ages, when it was grown more widely than it is today, and anyone who has tasted them should understand why. The service tree provided rowanberries, and even the berberry was used as food.

Medlar *Fig.* I.

Pl. 73

Portugal,
Pear-Quince.
Fig. II.

Portugal,
Apple-Quince.
Fig. III.

Seruice *Fig.* IIII.

English,
Quince.
Fig. V.

Berberry

Fig. VI.

'NOTTINGHAM'
(*MESPILUS GERMANICA*)

RIGHT: Of the two medlar varieties grown today, the 'Nottingham' is by far the more popular. It has smaller fruit than the 'Dutch', but many more of them. Medlars are still something of an acquired taste, but they still provide us with a small, and highly ornamental tree.

'DUTCH' (*MESPILUS GERMANICA*)

OPPOSITE: This has larger fruit than the 'Nottingham' medlar, but not as many of them. Some aficionados think its flavour is inferior but, as Edward Bunyard suggested, 'as [I] cannot appreciate this fruit, [I] should personally consider them equal in unpleasantness'.

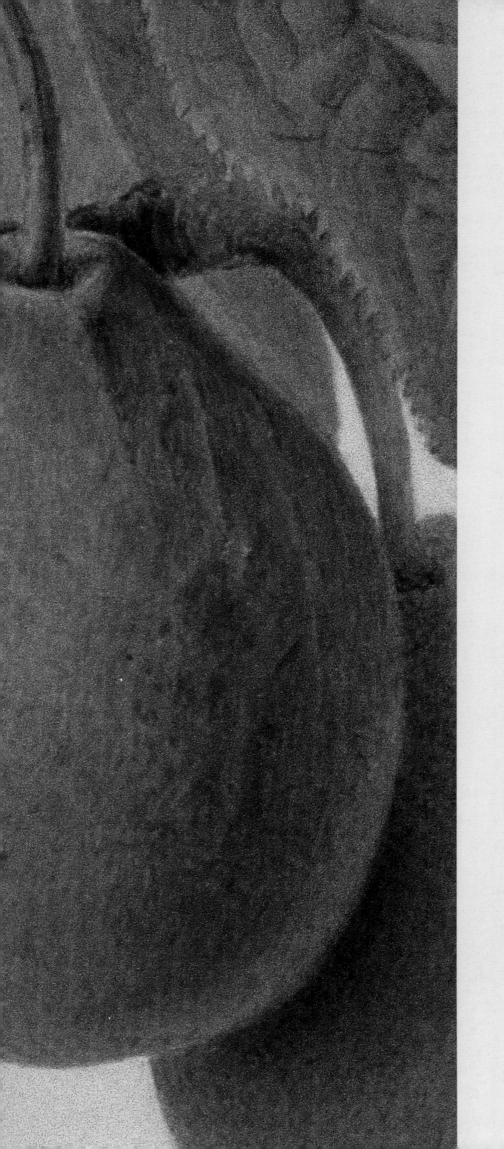

2:Stone

Primordian
July 1.

Plate XX.

Jean Hative June 9.th

Fig: II.

South East wall 30 Deg

Fig: I.

Morocco.
July 14. E. Wall.

Fig: III.

Orlean's July 10.

S. W. wall 40 Deg.

A   B

Fig: III.

Imperial
July 25
N.W. 45.
Deg:

Fig: V.

Fothering ham
or Sheen Plumb.
July 14 S.E. wall
20 Deg.

Violet July 15. West Wall.

Fig: VII.

Fig: VI.

La Royal
July 20
S.E. 40 Deg.

Fig: VIII.

B. Langley delin:

Bowles Sculp

The *Rosaceae* family also harbours the *Prunus* genus. These well-loved fruit trees and shrubs are grown throughout the temperate zones of the northern hemisphere, often as much for their beautiful spring blossoms as the delicious edible fruits. The genus is divided into four groups: one for plums and apricots; another for peaches, nectarines and almonds; a third for sweet and acid cherries; and the last for the wild 'bird' cherries. The mulberry, which has numerous pips instead of a stone, belongs to the *Moraceae* family, along with the fig and (somewhat incongruously) the cannabis plant. It is quite often cultivated for its sheer beauty as a tree rather than for the commercial value of its fruit.

The plum has (deservedly) been a popular fruit for hundreds of years and, like its relation the apple, has been eaten since prehistoric times. There are more varieties of plums than any other stone fruit, with a total in excess of two thousand. Alexander the Great is said to have introduced them to Europe from Syria or Persia, where the damson plum had long been grown, while Ancient Mesopotamian and Assyrian records both mention their cultivation. Like the cherry, the plum is one of the earliest trees to bear fruit in the summer, and the blossom from its typically low and spreading branches is often used as decoration, especially in Japan, whose native plum is *Prunus salicina*. On th other hand, the plum tree's fruit must be one of nature's greatest rewards to gardeners, particularly a ripe and juicy gage. Plums are very adaptable – though stewed plums, plum pudding, plum tarts, plum jam and even plum wine are all ways of making the least likable cooking plum into something worthwhile, none of these approach the delight of the truly ripe dessert fruit.

The cultivated plum, *P. domestica*, which is not found in the wild, is the result of many years of painstaking hybridization by fruit growers. Prehistoric lake sites in Switzerland have yielded the stones of other plums but not *P. domestica*, suggesting that it was a later introduction or hybridization. However, several other *Prunus* species with plum-like fruits are native to northern Asia and Europe, such as *P. spinosa* (the blackthorn or sloe), which is confined to Europe, and *P. insititia* (damsons, bullaces and, in France, mirabelles), which extends from the Himalayas to North Africa and throughout Europe to the south of Scotland. Strangely, it is not the northern form of *P. insititia* from which the British damson is descended, but one that developed around Damascus many hundreds of years ago. It is from the word

'Damascus' that the name 'damascene' arose, which then became corrupted to 'damson'. In contrast to this, the bullace (*P. insititia*) is the only native, wild British plum.

The true origin of the cultivated plum lies in southern Russia, where the fruits of *P. cerasifera* (the 'Cherry Plum' or myrobalan) were eaten, gathered and later grown by tribesmen. There are two types of myrobalan, one bearing red fruits and one bearing yellow, and it is now seen throughout Europe and beyond. Its ubiquity is due to its suitability for use as a rootstock of the domestic plum tree. Nurserymen find it very easy to propagate, as it produces abundant 'suckers', arising from adventitious buds on the roots. However, this suckering is a double-edged sword for gardeners, as even when the plum tree dies of old age the myrobalan rootstock will continue to live, usually sending up a profusion of suckers. The Romans' love of plums and interest in their cultivation is described by Pliny the Elder in Book XXIII of his great encyclopedia, *Naturalis Historia*, and it is probably thanks to the genetic tinkering of these early Roman fruit growers that we have so many varieties today.

Within *P. domestica* we find plums and gages. This distinction between plums and gages is purely British, as they were divided by their quality, and therefore use. Plums were employed for cooking, bottling, jamming, etc., while gages (the true aristocrats) were for dessert. This distinction has more or less disappeared and modern cultivars are largely dual-purpose. As Edward Bunyard said, 'the Victorians [plums] and their like may well remain in the kitchen, very welcome when cooked, but hardly up to the best standard of the dessert'. When you taste a true gage, you will understand why.

Gages came to Britain from France in the late fifteenth or early sixteenth century and were called 'Reine Claude', after Queen Claude, wife of King François I of France. Only later did they become 'gages', named 'Green Gage' as a compliment to Sir William Gage, who introduced them to England in 1725. These original gages are small, round and green, with a superb flavour unlike any other plum. Oddly enough, it is found in the scent of the iris known as *Iris graminea* – nature often plays tricks like this. Hybrids that have been bred using the 'Green Gage' as one parent, and which broadly possess its flavour, usually carry the word 'gage' in their name. Thus, we find 'Cambridge Gage', the four 'Transparent' gages and the French hybrid 'Reine Claude de Bavay', amongst others. The 'Transparents' arose from trees brought to Britain from France, by Thomas Rivers, the famous English nurseryman. He found them growing in the

DAMSON 'SHROPSHIRE' (*PRUNUS INSITITIA*)

OPPOSITE: For some inexplicable reason, this is also listed as the 'Prune' damson and the 'Cheshire' damson. The likely explanation is that it originated in the wild as a seedling and was circulated, as it were, privately from person to person. The inevitable result of this is a large number of acquired names.

Damas d'Espagne.

Lafay nursery near Paris, where they were labelled 'Reine Claude Diaphane', the '*diaphane*' referring to the translucent nature of the skin. The trees didn't take kindly to England and neither grew (nor fruited) satisfactorily. However, Rivers sowed stones he had saved from the few trees that had fruited, and in 1866 he selected and retained three of the resulting seedlings. He subsequently named one 'Early Transparent Gage'. This fruited earlier than the parent, to which he had given the English name 'Transparent Gage'. 'Late Transparent Gage' was another seedling, and the third one he called 'Golden Transparent Gage'. Thus arrived some of the best-flavoured gages there have ever been, all of which have translucent skin, allowing you to see the outline of the stone when the fruit is held up to the light.

Gages are true connoisseurs' fruits but, they are not difficult to grow, given adequate cross-pollination and frost protection during blossom. By contrast, the damson plum (*P. insititia*) is best not eaten immediately and usually requires treatment of some kind before consumprion. These are culinary fruit and, as hinted at in the name ('Damson' being a derivative of Damascus in Syria), were first used in an extensive way by the ancient peoples of the Middle East. They are superb – damson jam is a class apart, and damson gin is an excellent alternative to sloe gin.

The people of the Middle East were also probably the first to make prunes by drying plums. Certain varieties of plum can be dried with little loss of their original plumpness and flavour. Prunes from the area around Agen in France have been considered the best for centuries and are now at the heart of a major industry in California. Due to the havoc that prunes can wreak upon the digestive system, these little 'black-coated workers' very soon became figures of fun; indeed, many people feel unable to face the day without their morning 'fix' of prunes or prune juice. Indeed, even the *Grete Herball* (printed by Peter Treueris in 1526) remarks that plums dried for fifteen days and then kept in syrup have the virtue of 'keeping the bowels smooth and polished'. Prunes, it would appear, have been doing sterling work for almost five hundred years. There are few other natural remedies that can boast such a long and active life.

Cherries are similar to plums in many ways. Their blossoms are almost synonymous with springtime, particularly in Japan, where the cherry or 'sakura' is an unofficial national symbol, celebrated in art and literature. The spring blooming of the trees draws thousands of tourists from across Japan, such is the cherry's esteemed place in the country's culture. However beautiful its blossom might be, the cherry's history is as complicated as that of

'DAMAS D'ESPAGNE' (*PRUNUS INSITITIA*)

OPPOSITE: This second-rate dessert variety is similar in size to a damson (which is hinted at in its name – 'damson', '*damas*', 'damascene'and 'damask' are all roughly derivatives of the same fruit). Damascus in Syria was the starting point, with the damascene, and this later became the damson. Little is known of this 'Spanish' damson, other than that it existed.

the plum, with a bewildering number of species, subspecies, varieties and cultivars. Until about forty years ago, just three varieties dominated the British cherry market. 'Early Rivers' started the season, 'Napoléon Bigarreau' came towards the end and, sandwiched between them, the classic, dark-crimson, almost black 'Waterloo', which shared its colour with a ripe 'Morello' cherry ('Waterloo's' flavour is out of this world). When these three varieties dominated, the cherry season (from early July) always seemed to be sunny. Maybe this is the memory playing tricks, recalling only the sunshine and seldom the rain.

The history of cherries as an edible fruit goes back many centuries. The Danes ate them in Mesolithic times, and so did the lake people of Switzerland. The oldest accounts of orchard cherry growing come from Mesopotamia in the eighth century BC. Our cultivated cherries derive from two species: *Prunus avium*, from which the sweet cherry has arisen; and *P. cerasus*, which is the acid or sour cherry, such as the 'Morello'. There are hybrids between the two, which in Britain are the 'Duke' varieties, and the 'Royales' or 'Anglaises' in France. Both are closer to acid cherries than sweet varieties. It seems likely that *P. avium*, the sweet cherry, came from the Black Sea or Caspian Sea region, while the sour cherry, *P. cerasus*, probably originates from between the Swiss Alps and the Adriatic Sea. However, there are also Chinese records dating from around four thousand years ago describing a fruit that sounds suspiciously like a cherry, so they could have started there and spread to Europe via Central Asia, the Middle East and the Mediterranean. Wild seedlings and suckers of *P. avium* have been used for centuries as rootstocks for cultivated cherry trees. Seedlings of *P. mahaleb*, originally from central and southern Europe, have also been used since the mid-nineteenth century, mostly in the USA and mainland Europe.

Recognizably different varieties of cherry appeared as early as the fifth century BC in Central Asia, where there was one variety called 'Ponticum'. The Romans also cultivated cherries, and there were several named varieties at the time of Pliny, who referred to 'Apronian' as the reddest, 'Lutatian' the darkest, 'Caecilian' as being round, 'Junian' as having a good flavour if eaten straight from the tree, and 'Duracina' as the best of all. John Gibson, author of 'The Fruit Gardene', writing in 1768, suggested that 'Apronian' was probably the Cluster cherry, 'Lutatian' the mazzard or gean (*P. avium*), 'Caecilian' was the Kentish or 'Common Red', 'Junian' could have been the French *guigne*, while 'Duracina' may

---

'DAMAS DE PROVENCE' (*PRUNUS INSITITIA*)

OPPOSITE: The main difference between damsons and plums is their size, shape and flavour. Damsons are also, along with bullaces and mirabelles, derived from *Prunus institia*. One damson in particular, 'Merryweather', is even considered to be a cross between a damson and a plum. However, the taste of the damson is quite distinct from that of the plum.

have become the firm-fleshed *bigarreau*, the English heart cherry. Evidence of *P. avium* cherries being eaten in Britain goes back to the Late Iron Age. Similarly, stones of *P. cerasus* came to light in a Middle Bronze Age site. Cherries were well established in Roman Britain and many varieties then came from abroad. John Gerard, the sixteenth-century English herbalist, mentioned 'Naples' from Italy and, early in the seventeenth century, John Parkinson listed thirty varieties. The variety 'John Tradescant' was almost identical to the fine black 'Noble' that was being grown commercially well into the twentieth century. John Tradescant the Elder, gardener to Charles I of England, originally imported this variety in the seventeenth century, which in the USA was known as 'Tradescant's Black Heart'. This sounds rather macabre, but many cherries are similarly named, on account of their heartlike shape (such as 'White Heart' and 'Elton Heart').

In more modern times, the USA and Canada have bred many excellent cultivars, 'Lambert' and 'Bing' being two of the most widely grown. Canada was responsible for the first self-fertile varieties, including 'Stella' and 'Sunburst'. Previously, a single sweet cherry tree would produce few (if any) fruits unless it was pollinated by another variety. Because of consumer preference, the black varieties are favoured for their softer, juicier and tastier fruits. There is probably also a feeling that the white varieties − with their partial covering of pink − are not quite ripe, whereas a shiny dark-purple, almost black cherry looks good enough to eat. Whatever the reason, there is virtually no call for new 'white' varieties, except for canning and other forms of processing.

Although the cherry is a popular fruit, its cultivation is fraught with problems. Until quite recently, cherry trees were enormous, too large for domestic gardens and uneconomic for commercial orchards. The major influence on the size and vigour of a tree is the rootstock upon which it grows, but in the cherry's case it is difficult to find one that is compatible with the scion (actual cherry variety) on a long-term basis. Usually, after about ten years, the union fails and the tree collapses. Belgium and Germany have bred several rootstocks which show real promise, and (Germany, in particular) has bred excellent dwarfing rootstocks for sweet cherries, which are undergoing trials in Britain, the USA and elsewhere. Cherries also suffer from splitting, as their skin absorbs more rainwater than they can use or transpire. In domestic gardens, covering the trees with polythene bags can solve the problem, but this is clearly inefficient in a

'WHITE DAMSON' (*PRUNUS INSITITIA*)
OPPOSITE: With the wealth of other damsons available, this really has little to recommend it beyond its unusual colour (for a damson). Unlike most others, the stone clings to the flesh, which is usually to the detriment of the variety. It has the virtue of being unusual in a collection of damsons, though.

'BLUE IMPERATRICE' (*PRUNUS DOMESTICA*)

ABOVE: Also known as 'Empress', or simply 'Impératrice', this is one of the latest-ripening plums, usually ready around mid-October. In fact, to catch it at its best it is suggested that it should be left on the tree until it has just started to shrivel (late October to early November), which is when Forsyth tells us that it will be at its sweetest.

'WILMOT'S EARLY VIOLET' (*PRUNUS DOMESTICA*)

RIGHT: Although he is not well documented, we do know that John Wilmot had an 'immense [60 acre/ 25 hectare] horticultural establishment' in Isleworth, Middlesex in the early nineteenth century. He is better known for growing 'extensive plantations' of strawberries here (such as the 'Wilmot's Superb'), along with fruit trees and shrubs.

commercial environment. An alternative answer would be to find the gene that controls skin porosity – another instance where GM could avoid years of work. Commercial cherry cultivation used to be common in northern Europe but, due to the problems of size and splitting, most of the crop is now produced by southern Europe and the USA. Cherries are best eaten immediately after picking, as they soon become flaccid. The best place to buy them is still in situ, at the farm shops where they were grown, but like many traditions this too is on the decline.

The summer cherry-picking season used to be a great time for students and other youngsters. Long, wooden fruit ladders had to be manhandled from tree to tree. When the picker approached the top of the tree and strained to reach the unreachable, the ladder often twisted, leaving them dangling underneath it, amidst howls of laughter from those at ground level. Great skill was then needed to get back on the correct side of the ladder without losing all the cherries or falling off and breaking your neck. Those halcyon days may be passing but the cherry remains a much-loved fruit, particularly by children, who will doubtless never tire of firing the pips at unsuspecting, unlucky passers-by.

Peaches and nectarines are also members of the *Prunus* genus. The most mouth-watering and decadent of fruits, they have been cultivated in Europe since the first century AD, although evidence of their cultivation in Britain is only forthcoming with the untimely demise of King John in 1216. He died from dysentery in Newark Castle, apparently after consuming a surfeit of green peaches and ale. It goes without saying that ripe peaches should not be green, so that could well provide a clue to the king's unpleasant end. Moving further back in time towards the peach's origin, it is understandable that many authorities assumed that the peach (*Prunus persica*) came from Persia or modern Iran; that, after all, is what '*persica*' means – 'of or pertaining to Persia'. This is not actually the case, because the peach and the nectarine both came from the China/Korea/Manchuria region. Like its cousin the cherry, accounts of the peach and the nectarine exist from as far back as four thousand years ago. How the misleading specific name came about is not certain, but it is likely that the Romans (or the Greeks before them) found the peach growing, or for sale, in Persia. Whatever the case, it is known that the peach came from the Far East and would have travelled along the silk route.

If fruit trees are propagated from seed, the resulting seedlings are a mixture of all the previous generations, but the peach seems (partially) to ignore this rule of nature. Trees grown from peach seeds nearly always produce remarkably

'LA ROYALE' (*PRUNUS DOMESTICA*)

OPPOSITE: Although it may look uninspiring, this plum is actually of the highest quality. It ripens in August/September and will often shrivel and remain on the tree when ripe. It is French in origin and goes back to at least 1724 (it is featured in Stephen Switzer's *Practical Fruit Gardener*). At one time it was grown in the Royal Garden at Hampton Court Palace, London.

high-quality and similar fruit, unlike apples and pears, and many excellent but nameless varieties have been produced in this way. The season of ripening is perhaps the greatest difference between them. Thus, genetically, the peach is a stable fruit, although it did have one important lapse in stability when it produced the nectarine. As with all sports, however, the two fruits are botanically the same. When the mutation originally occurred is not known, but it must have been long ago, as accounts verify that (like the peach) the nectarine came from China. The strangest thing about this mutation is that it can, theoretically, recur at any time. Many older gardening books tell growers to ensure that, when propagating, the shoots are taken from trees that are stable, and completely peach or completely nectarine – a century ago it was quite common for trees of either fruit to produce shoots carrying both peaches and nectarines. Even single fruits with areas of both shiny and downy skin were not uncommon. Seedlings behaved like this, as well. Furthermore, if a peach is crossed with a nectarine, the progeny will all be peaches (i.e. they will all have downy skin). It is only in subsequent generations and after self-pollination (selfing) that shiny-skinned fruits will appear, which clearly shows that it is a recessive gene that causes the smooth skin.

During the seventeenth century, many new kinds and varieties of fruit, including peaches and nectarines, reached Britain from the rest of Europe, and this is when names that are still familiar today begin to arise. For example, the 'Elruge' nectarine is still listed, and is a good variety even by today's standards. However, the peach and nectarine are really at their happiest in a Mediterranean climate, and are only cultivable in northern Europe if protected or where there is an especially favourable microclimate. It is not that they are winter-tender, but they require a longer and hotter summer than cooler regions can provide. It wasn't until Thomas Rivers bred his famous 'Hawk' series of peaches in the early twentieth century that they came within the scope of growers and gardeners in less suitable areas. This collection of peaches included 'Goshawk', 'Kestrel', 'Peregrine' and 'Sea Eagle', the latter three of which are still grown today; indeed, 'Peregrine' remains the most reliable outdoor peach in northern climes. Nectarines are usually more colourful than peaches, having more red in the skin, and are also slightly smaller. Some people say they also have a different flavour.

The commercial growing of peaches has now passed from the greenhouses of northern Europe to the

'ISLE VERTE' (*PRUNUS DOMESTICA*)

OPPOSITE: Apart from its portrait in the *Nouveau Duhamel*, there are no reliable accounts of this variety. The fruit's shape is similar to several cooking varieties in existence today, such as the 'Yellow Egg' plums, the 'Giant Prune' and 'Purple Pershore', which would indicate that its main use is in the kitchen rather than at the dinner table.

Mediterranean outdoors, southern Africa and the southern states of the USA. They reached America with Spanish explorers in the sixteenth century and caught on very quickly. There was a two-way trade in varieties and many of the new American examples found their way to Europe, including 'Hale's Early', the 'Amsden' series and 'Rochester'. Today, California is the most productive peach area in the USA, breeding many of the commercial varieties grown there. In Europe the lion's share of the market goes to the Mediterranean countries. Mention must finally be made of the peach's gorgeous, deep-pink blossom. Sadly, the flowers appear very early in the spring – in March, or even late February – and are frequently ruined by frost, but such is its beauty that, once seen, a peach tree in flower is unlikely to be forgotten.

'Apricots are plums concealed beneath a peach's coat' – so said Dr Muffet, author of the nursery rhyme that begins 'Little Miss Muffet sat on her tuffet...' But Dr Muffet also wrote extensively in the seventeenth century regarding the medicinal properties and other virtues of the apricot. In fact, his description above fits apricots (*Prunus armeniaca*) very adequately, because they do look like furry plums or small peaches. They also share a misleading specific name with peaches: although they are found growing wild in Armenia, the apricot originated in China, home of so many valuable and beautiful plants.

To an extent, the whole range of *Prunus* stone fruits are compatible with one another, in that a small degree of success is possible if they are inter bred. For the most part, the offspring – grandly called 'inter-specific hybrids' – are best described as mongrels rather than upmarket crossbreeds, but some strange results are possible. For instance, there was a strange fruit called a plumcot, which was the offspring of a plum and an apricot, and another was the peach-apricot. Whatever their end, most only had curiosity value. It does, however, illustrate the ease with which nature can cross borders, and the genus *Prunus* has proved very productive in this respect. Due to a lack of earlier evidence, it is likely that apricots did not reach Britain until the mid-fifteenth century. By the turn of that century, they were still only being grown in the gardens of large country houses, where sunny walls provided the trees with the protection they needed in order to thrive. In common with the peach and nectarine, apricots are perfectly winter-hardy but bloom very early in the spring. Therefore, unless protected, they are likely to be caught by frost when in flower, thus putting

CHERRY PLUM (*PRUNUS CERASIFERA*)

OPPOSITE: The myrobalan is a small red or yellow plum, its common name being Cherry Plum. It was used mainly as a windbreak tree and a rootstock for plums and gages. Many people who come across it today in gardens are actually looking at suckers sent up by the roots of an old (and often dead) plum tree. The fruits can be pleasant in their own right when stewed.

'GREEN GAGE' (*PRUNUS DOMESTICA*)

ABOVE AND OPPOSITE: This is one of the most famous plums of all time, and also one of the oldest – a French high-quality dessert variety. In France it is grown as 'Reine Claude', named after Claude, the wife of King François I, but when it was brought to England in about 1725, it was renamed 'Green Gage' (after William Gage, the Englishman who introduced it), which remains the English name for the 'Reine Claude' dessert plum today. It was the original gage, the name under which most dessert plums went until the twentieth century. The 'Green Gage' is still widely cultivated in France and many seedlings exist, such as 'Reine Claude de Bavay'.

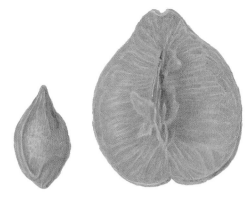

an end to the year's crop. Apricots flower even earlier than peaches or nectarines, so they need extra-special care.

'Moor Park' is the oldest known variety still in existence and remains the most widely planted in Britain. Interestingly, it is thought that 'Moor Park' is possibly a seedling from a hybrid peach-apricot. 'Breda' is also listed in a few catalogues but, as is so often the case with very old varieties, a certain amount of doubt surrounds the true identity of trees sold as 'Breda' today. Like the peach, apricots are rarely grown in the colder climes of northern Europe because of their early flowering and their need for longer and hotter summers. Fruit is usually imported from the Mediterranean, southern Africa, New Zealand and the southern states of the USA – both fresh and dried, it is so cheap as to render production elsewhere completely uneconomical.

Finally, we have the mulberry, which has pips instead of a stone and belongs to the *Moraceae* family. There are two important species that concern us here: the white mulberry, *Morus alba*, and the black mulberry, *Morus nigra*. (There is also a red mulberry, *Morus rubra,* but it is grown for its decorative value rather than for its fruit.) The white mulberry fruit comes a very poor second to the black, but is important in silk production, its leaves being the staple diet of silk worms. Its fruits are edible but very inferior and, as long ago as the mid-seventeenth century, there was a use for the juice of the mulberry. In much the same way that antifreeze was illegally added to certain European wines in the late twentieth century in an attempt to 'improve' them, the juice of the mulberry was used for transforming the appearance of cider, white wine and even vinegar into that of red wine, and only when the first mouthful was taken did the awful truth dawn upon the unsuspecting drinker.

To find the origin of the black mulberry, one must travel to Central Asia, the region around the Caucasus Mountains and into Nepal. Black mulberry seeds have been found in archaeological sites all over the area, into the Fertile Crescent and beyond, into Egypt. Mulberries are mentioned in the Bible, particularly in the Psalms, but it is not clear to which species the text is referring. The sole importance of the white mulberry tree was in silk production, as mentioned above. It first reached Greece and then Rome during the two hundred years before Christ, so it seems likely that the same period also saw the beginnings of mulberry cultivation in the Mediterranean.

The first occasion we can be sure that it is the black mulberry that is being referred to is in the first century AD,

'COE'S GOLDEN DROP' (*PRUNUS DOMESTICA*)

OPPOSITE: 'Coe's Golden Drop' is one of the great English dessert plums, stretching back to Jervaise Coe of Bury St Edmunds, who bred it in 1800. Possessing a rich flavour, with a touch of apricot, it is one of the few plums that will stay in good condition on the tree for a couple of weeks, and can also be stored for about a month after picking.

Mirabelle.

when Pliny mentions that its juice can often stain the hands. Indeed, anyone who has handled them will know what he means, as it is almost impossible to avoid the staining because the mulberry fruit's skin is extremely thin. (Helpfully, Pliny continues to explain that the best way of removing the stain is with the juice of an unripe berry.) The period of Roman occupation is also the same general time during which mulberries would first have reached Britain from Italy. It is assumed that it is the trees that were imported, because the mulberry was not a native of Britain at the time and the tender fruits would never have survived the journey.

The black mulberry (*M. nigra*) is grown for its fruit but it is rather sad that more uses cannot be found for its berries, as they grow plentifully and with great ease. The fruits look like a coarse blackberry and, when fully grown, turn from pale green to a very dark red. Unhappily, the berries have two faults: their terrific staining power (as described above), and the size of their pips, which are too large and numerous for comfort. The staining has a secondary curse because the ripe berries are a favourite food of blackbirds – the time between eating and expelling seems to be minimal, and expulsion always seems to take place near a washing line full of almost-dry, almost-always-white garments.

The only berry that surpasses the mulberry in the staining department is the elderberry, and this could also explain the mulberry's lack of popularity as a garden tree. Elderberry wine has been popular for centuries, but the mulberry's usefulness as a fruit is ultimately rather limited. Adding mulberries as flavouring and colouring to cooked apples makes a refreshing change, but the pips have to be endured and therefore it is one of the few fruits that has undergone no change whatsoever over the years. There are no varieties – simply clones of improved performance. This is mainly due to its lack of commercial use and, hence, the need to improve it. The other reason is that nowadays it is planted for the beauty of the tree rather than for its fruits, which are purely a bonus. A mulberry tree's most important virtue is the ripe old age to which it will grow. There are accounts of several that have exceeded six hundred years – one that was planted at the Draper's Hall in the City of London in 1364 only died in 1969, and some very old white mulberry trees at Hatfield House in Hertfordshire were reputedly planted by King James I in the early seventeenth century. It is only fitting that such a noble tree be known for a venerated product like silk, so maybe the mulberry is best left to the silkworms.

'YELLOW PLUM' (*PRUNUS INSITITIA*)
OPPOSITE: The mirabelle, or 'Yellow Plum', is strictly speaking a group of plums rather than an actual variety. It is related to the damson and bullace but does not taste the same. It is essentially a French fruit and is rarely seen in England (where damsons and bullaces are more popular).

'KENTISH BIGARREAU' (*PRUNUS AVIUM*)

ABOVE: Also known as 'Bigarreau Kentish', 'Biggerow' or 'Big Arrow', commercial growers often referred to this cherry variety as 'Amber Heart', or even just 'Amber'. Although originally of Italian origin, the 'Kentish Bigarreau' was a popular variety with English growers in the mid-twentieth century.

'FLORENCE' (*PRUNUS AVIUM*)

OPPOSITE: 'Florence' is another variety whose descriptions vary alarmingly. However, all accounts agree that it came to England (Essex) from the Florence/Pistoia region of Italy early in the nineteenth century. Bliss says in *The Fruit Grower's Instructor* (1825) that, in the UK, it cropped better and was larger when fan-trained to a sunny wall.

'ROYALE ORDINAIRE' (*PRUNUS AVIUM*)

ABOVE: Common sense would lead us to presume that 'Royale Ordinaire' and 'Royale' are the same variety. However, 'Royale' is actually synonymous with 'Royale Tardive' (*tardive* means 'late'), as well as 'Cherry Duke'. It then appears that 'Cherry Duke' is the same variety as 'Jeffrey's Duke'. Such were the ways of fruit naming in the late eighteenth century.

'BELLE DE ROCMONT' (*PRUNUS AVIUM*)

LEFT: The 'Belle de Rocmont' was formerly known as 'Bigarreau Gros Coeuret', but also (among other names) 'Pigeon Heart'. The naming of varieties in the distant past has led to much confusion, because in the seventeenth century it seems there was also a plum called 'Pigeon Heart' ('Coeur de Pigeon'), in the *Potager du Roi* (King's Kitchen Garden) at Versailles.

'MORELLO' (*PRUNUS CERASUS*)

ABOVE: Along with *Prunus avium*, *P. cerasus* is one of the two species from which our cultivated cherries are derived. This standard sour cherry has been grown since at least 1629, and is one of very few fruits that will grow satisfactorily when trained to a north-facing wall. What this really means is that, because it is not a dessert variety, the 'Morello' does not need the sunshine to ripen it.

'MAY DUKE' (*PRUNUS AVIUM*)

RIGHT: This variety is generally considered to be the same as 'Cerise d'Angleterre Hâtive', yet Bliss (1825) makes no mention of this. He does, however, give its season as early June when fan-trained against a warm wall, and Bliss regards it as one of England's finest sweet cherries, with an excellent flavour. 'Cerise Royale Hâtive' is another alias for 'May Duke', which demonstrates how difficult it is to nail down firmly the identity of a fruit that can be grown in many different countries. This name was adopted in France, when it was introduced there from England in the middle of the eighteenth century. Unfortunately, its true origin is uncertain and it could even be that 'May Duke' is a corruption of 'Médoc', the area of France from which it originally came.

'EARLY RIVERS' (*PRUNUS AVIUM*)

ABOVE: One of the best-known cherries from the famous Rivers nursery at Sawbridgeworth in Hertfordshire, the 'Early Rivers' was introduced in about 1872. It was the standard, early, sweet variety grown in Kent, and elsewhere, for the best part of a hundred years. Its enormous trees and irregular cropping contributed to its downfall, however.

'WATERLOO' (*PRUNUS AVIUM*)

OPPOSITE: Probably the finest-flavoured black, sweet cherry, and another of the masterpieces of Thomas Andrew Knight, the 'Waterloo' is so named because it carried fruit for the first time in 1815, a few weeks after the Battle of Waterloo. Though it it is possibly the most delicious of all cherries, unfortunately it is no longer reliable enough for wide commercial planting.

'RED MAGDALENE' (*PRUNUS PERSICA*)

ABOVE: The peach is a very ancient fruit. It came originally from China – not Persia, as its specific name *persica* suggests. 'Red Magdalene' is therefore an old member of an old family, and 'Madeleine Rouge' was one of the varieties recommended by de la Quintinye. Another of its names was 'Madeleine de Courson', presumably after the chateau and village southwest of Paris.

'LA NOBLESSE' (*PRUNUS PERSICA*)

OPPOSITE: A peach with a French name could justifiably be thought to come from France. But in the case of 'La Noblesse' (or, simply, 'Noblesse') it is actually a Dutch variety, which in all probability came to England via one of the many Dutch merchants trading with Britain during the reigns of Queen Anne and George I.

Pavie de Pompone.

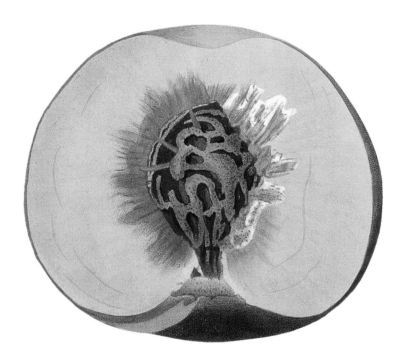

'ROSANNA' (*PRUNUS PERSICA*)

ABOVE: This is a very productive variety, cropping well both as
a free-standing tree and trained. The 'Rosanna' is another variety
that was often mistaken for another, and vice versa (in this case
the other variety is 'Pavie Jaune', also known as 'Alberge Jaune').

'PAVIE DE POMPONE' (*PRUNUS PERSICA*)

OPPOSITE: *'Pavie'* is the French word for a clingstone peach,
and this variety has an enormous fruit some 30–35cm (12–14in)
round, a stone from which probably gave rise to Thomas Rivers'
'Princess of Wales'. Unfortunately, it needs a warm and sunny
summer in order to give of its best – then, its vinous, sugary and
musky flavour is superb. At other times, it is insipid and barely
worth eating.

'PAVIE JAUNE' (*PRUNUS PERSICA*)

ABOVE AND RIGHT: Also known as 'Alberge Jaune', this is a latish variety that ripens at the beginning of September. It has a rich, vinous flavour and, in warmer areas, succeeds well as a free-standing tree in the open garden. The 'Pavie Jaune' is also found listed (erroneously) under the name of 'Rosanna'. Both are mentioned and treated separately by Jean-Baptiste de la Quintinye. The word '*pavie*' was described by de la Quintinye's translators, London & Wise, as one 'cleaving to the stone', which is much more descriptive. So here we have a yellow (*jaune*) clingstone peach.

'TETON DE VENUS' (*PRUNUS PERSICA*)

ABOVE: This very old French variety was known in 1667 and grown in England in the eighteenth century as 'Tueton de Venice'. It is sometimes considered the same as 'Late Admirable', though this is incorrect. The 'Téton de Vénus' (meaning 'Venus' breast') has rich, melting flesh, with a good vinous taste. Ripening in late September, this variety has a distinct point at the flower end of the fruit.

'PECHE CARDINALE' (*PRUNUS PERSICA*)

OPPOSITE: Apart from being decorative, it is not very clear what other values this peach possesses. Neither Forsyth nor de la Quintinye mention 'Pêche Cardinale' in their lists of recommended varieties, and R.D. Blackmore (nineteenth-century novelist and fruit grower at Teddington, Middlesex for forty years) contributed notes to the last edition of Hogg's *Fruit Manual* on his experience of pear and peach varieties at his nursery, many of which were highly unfavourable. He described the 'Stump the World' as 'utterly useless', for example, and one fears that this variety would have fared no better.

NECTARINE VARIETIES FROM BROOKSHAW'S *POMONA BRITTANICA* (1812)
ABOVE: 'Clarmont', 'Homerton's White', 'Ford's Black', 'Genoa'.
OPPOSITE: 'Vermash', 'Violette Hâtive', 'Red Roman', 'North's Scarlet', 'Elruge', 'Peterborough'.
Although it came from China, we do not know exactly when or where the original nectarine
appeared, but we can say that it began as a sport'(or mutant) on a peach tree. Therefore, a nectarine
is simply a hairless peach fruit that appeared on a peach tree, and botanically it is still a peach
(*Prunus persica*), though obviously not structurally the same. The strange thing is that peach trees still
occasionally send out a branch that produces nectarines, and vice versa, and you can even get fruits
that are partially hairy.

'VIOLETTE HATIVE' (*PRUNUS PERSICA* VAR. *NECTARINA*)

ABOVE: Normally accepted as the very best of the early nectarines, this French variety dates back to at least 1629. The 'Violette Hâtive' is praised highly by de la Quintinye, and in the mid-nineteenth century its praises stretched as far as the United States. What a shame that a variety which was held in such high esteem for nearly four hundred years has all but disappeared.

'ELRUGE' (*PRUNUS PERSICA* VAR. *NECTARINA*)

LEFT: The name of this nectarine is a twist on the habit of naming a plant after oneself. With the addition of an 'e' (presumably to improve the pronunciation of the word), 'Elruge' is simply the breeder's name (Gurle) spelled backwards, though strangely Gurle's name is also recorded as 'Garrle' and 'Gourle'. It is still listed, though, and the 'Elruge' remains a good variety, even by today's standards.

NECTARINE VARIETIES FROM
LANGLEY'S *POMONA* (1729)
OPPOSITE: Again, we see that as early as
the eighteenth century there was quite a
wide choice of nectarine varieties. What is
encouraging, and surprising, is that heated
greenhouses must have existed then (and
been in quite wide use) in the large
country houses of the time.

'THE OLD NEWINGTON'
(*PRUNUS PERSICA*
VAR. *NECTARINA*)
LEFT: It is fascinating to look at the
different names that have been given to
the same variety over the years.
'Newington' could well refer to the village
in Kent, England, where the variety started,
yet we find that it was also called
'Anderdon's' and 'Rough Roman'.

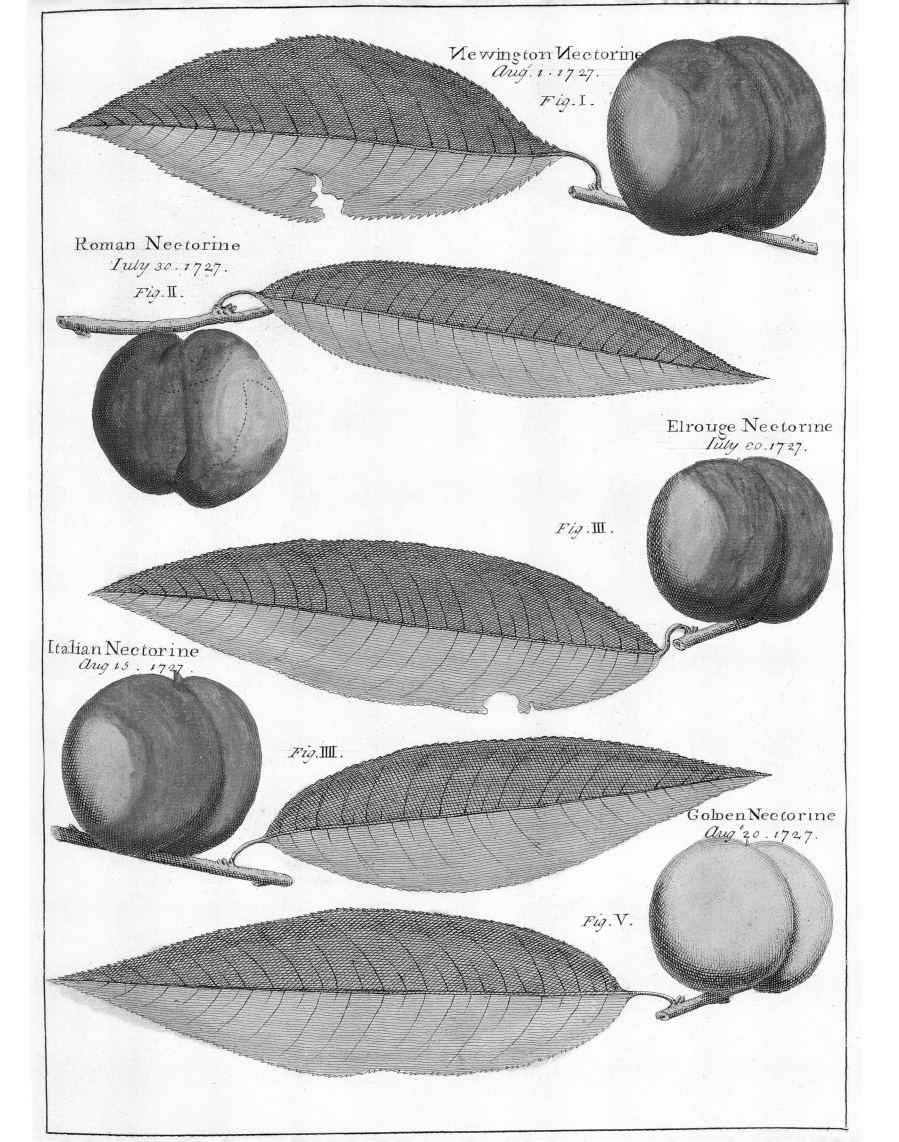

Newington Nectorine
Aug. 1. 1727.
Fig. I.

Roman Nectorine
Iuly 30. 1727.
Fig. II.

Elrouge Nectorine
Iuly 30. 1727.

Fig. III.

Italian Nectorine
Aug 15. 1727.

Fig. IIII.

Golden Nectorine
Aug. 20. 1727.

Fig. V.

'FAIRCHILD'S EARLY' (*PRUNUS PERSICA* VAR. *NECTARINA*)

ABOVE: Thomas Fairchild held a firm belief in the Resurrection. This conviction was so strong that he left £100 in his will to the trustees of a charity school and the churchwardens of Shoreditch so that a sermon could be preached on Whit Tuesday afternoon for ever more. The subject of this sermon was to be either 'The Wonderful Works of God in the Creation' or 'The Certainty of the Resurrection of the Dead'. By profession, Fairchild was a nurseryman, and lived in Hoxton, London.

'WHITE' (*PRUNUS PERSICA* VAR. *NECTARINA*)

OPPOSITE: Although its name came from the colour of both its skin and flesh, the 'White' was still a high-quality nectarine, and was held in much esteem early in the nineteenth century. In fact, its pale appearance was turned into an ornamental virtue – in contrast to the almost universal red/yellow/orange colouring of other varieties.

'NANCY' (*PRUNUS ARMENIACA*)

ABOVE: The peach-apricot hybrid is a strange beast; more of a curio than a valuable fruit or variety. Some authorities believe that the 'Moor Park' apricot is a hybrid of 'Nancy', but Hogg is quite certain that, although similar, the two are quite distinct.

'MOOR PARK' (*PRUNUS ARMENIACA*)

LEFT: The best-known and most widely grown apricot in the UK, 'Moor Park' is also very popular in the US. It is almost certain that Lord Anson was the first person to cultivate it in England, in about 1760 at his home, Moor Park, near Watford. It is believed to have come from a peach/apricot stone.

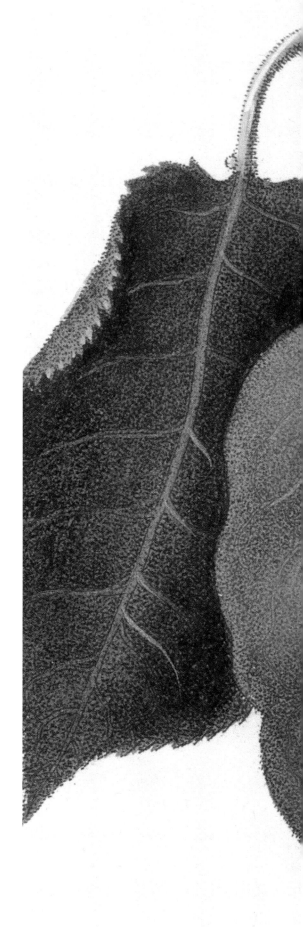

'BREDA' (*PRUNUS ARMENIACA*)

ABOVE: Another very old and famous apricot, but again it seems to vary (according to its source) both in appearance and flavour. This gives rise to the belief that not all specimens are correctly named. This apricot reached England from Breda in Holland (hence the name), but originally came from North Africa. The fruit is large, soft and juicy.

'ALBICOCCA DI GERMANIA' (*PRUNUS ARMENIACA*)

RIGHT: This Italian varietal name means 'German Apricot', which tells us that the apricot was cultivated in northern Continental countries. This variety is therefore perfectly winter-hardy and clearly thrives in the warm summers that exist there, although it would almost certainly thrive best in a glasshouse, as it does in Britain.

'MUSCH MUSCH' (*PRUNUS ARMENIACA*)

ABOVE: Some say this apricot takes its name from the Turkish town of Musch, although another contender is an Egyptian oasis called Mich-mich, where the inhabitants grew it from the early nineteenth century. Its origins are clearly from warmer countries, and its early flowering makes 'Musch Musch' difficult to grow in temperate regions without protection.

'PRECOCE' (*PRUNUS ARMENIACA*)

OPPOSITE: Synonymous with the oddly named 'Red Masculine' apricot, 'Précoce' was first mentioned by Parkinson in 1629, since when virtually every writer has included it. The small and early-ripening fruits (barely 1.5cm/1in across) are tender, juicy and sweet. Forsyth names it simply as 'Masculine', though the two are clearly the same variety.

'VIOLET' (*PRUNUS ARMENIACA*)

ABOVE: The kindest way to describe apricot nomenclature is to say that it is 'confused'. But when you consider that before we had modern breeding programmes many varieties looked frighteningly similar, this is hardly surprising. Many seedlings therefore bear a striking resemblance both to their parents and cousins. The same mixed scenario exists with peaches.

'NOIR' (*PRUNUS ARMENIACA*)

OPPOSITE: Also known as the 'Black' apricot, Hogg describes the 'Noir' as 'tasteless, insipid and quite worthless to eat', which sums it up really. It is small – barely bigger than a plum – purple on the sunny side, and reddish elsewhere (it even has reddish flesh). It would make quite a good ornamental tree for gardens, though.

Abricot Noir.

BLACK MULBERRY (*MORUS NIGRA*)

ABOVE AND OPPOSITE: Unlike the white mulberry, which is grown to feed silkworms, the black ('common') mulberry is grown predominantly for its fruit (or more accurately, it is usually grown as an ornamental tree). It can grow to a ripe old age – certainly several hundred years old. The fruit only forms properly in warmer climates, but grows plentifully and with ease. Although few varietal names exist, unusually the mulberry opposite is called 'Murier de Virginie'.

RED MULBERRY (*MORUS RUBRA*)

ABOVE: The red mulberry is a native of (and is solely grown in) the United States, where the fruits used to be fed to pigs and poultry. This variety has more ornamental and academic value than it does any practical use as an edible fruit.

WHITE MULBERRY (*MORUS ALBA*)

OPPOSITE: This is the other mulberry that is cultivated. However, it is grown primarily for its leaves, which are used as food for rearing silk worms, the popular name for the larvae of *Bombyx mori*. The fruits of the white mulberry are largely valueless.

3:Berry

Unfortunately, most people's first impression of a blackcurrant bush is the almost overpowering smell of tomcats. The main source of the smell is the buds, and the strength of the odour can almost make one feel a little sick. Extraordinarily, the same buds are cultivated in special plantations and collected during the winter for use in the perfume and pharmaceutical industries. Experts disagree vigorously as to the correct place of the genus *Ribes* − which includes blackcurrants, redcurrants and gooseberries − within the plant world, but the position of the Royal Horticultural Society in London is quite clear. In their *A–Z Encyclopedia of Garden Plants*, *Ribes* is classified as *Grossulariaceae/Saxifragaceae* − a happy agreement between the two contestants.

Ribes species do not appear to have been cultivated until comparatively recently. Unlike other fruits, there is no evidence of *Ribes'* cultivation in Ancient Greece or Rome. Early in the seventeenth century, the English writer John Gerard included them with gooseberries as 'another sort, altogether without prickles, whose fruit is verie small, lesser by much than the common kind, but of a perfect red colour'. The word 'currant' itself is a corruption of 'Corinth', the name of the Greek province where dried currants came from. Incidentally, dried 'currants' are not currants at all, but the dried fruit of a variety of small, fruited grape.

Most *Ribes* species are native to the temperate zones of the northern hemisphere, although a few occur in the mountains of Central and South America. Currants and gooseberries are the only useful fruiting members of *Ribes*. They are cultivated almost exclusively north of the Equator, predominantly in western, central and eastern Europe, but very rarely in the far north or south of Europe. Much current research into blackcurrants involves experimentation with different *Ribes* species in order to introduce desirable characteristics to fruiting varieties. For instance, *R. bracteosum* is favoured for bunch length, and *R. sanguinium* for aphid resistance. The other curse of the blackcurrant is a pest called 'big bud mite', which carries the 'reversion' virus disease. This could be controlled by the introduction of some gooseberry 'blood' (juice), which is not attacked by the pest. There is already a new variety, 'Foxendale', which is showing excellent resistance to 'big bud mite'. Greater frost resistance has been introduced by bringing a Finnish variety called 'Brodtorp' into the breeding programme, but probably the greatest modern change in commercial blackcurrant growing is the method of picking, which was traditionally carried out by gangs of female pickers. They were often

'WHITE DUTCH' (*RIBES RUBRUM* (*W*))

OPPOSITE: Another name for this excellent whitecurrant is 'White Grape' (if 'white' is the appropriate word). Whitecurrants are generally sweeter than the red ones, of which they are a colourless variety, so are favoured for eating as a dessert and for winemaking. The other notable variety is 'Blanche Versailles'.

employed from the start of the strawberry-picking season in June to the end of the apple and pear season in October. The subsequent introduction of the mechanical blackcurrant harvester signalled the departure of the pickers, and at a stroke one of the most productive and entertaining sources of a young farm student's education in 'life' disappeared.

Today, virtually the whole of the commercial blackcurrant crop in Great Britain goes for processing, much of it ending up in bottles of blackcurrant squashes such as Ribena. The fresh-fruit market is largely satisfied by 'pick-your-owns', farm shops and, more recently, farmers' markets. The main benefit of blackcurrant drinks such as Ribena is that the fruit is bursting with vitamin C – fresh fruit and vegetables are the main source of this valuable vitamin, which protects against conditions such as scurvy. Unsurprisingly, the original uses for blackcurrants were mainly medicinal. For instance, the juice has a relaxing effect on sore throats, for which blackcurrant lozenges have remained a very popular remedy. This use gave blackcurrants the unlikely name of 'quinsy berries', quinsy being a form of tonsillitis. Along with many fruits, blackcurrants have always played a part in the beverage department (alcoholic and non-alcoholic). The juice was regularly used to colour or flavour inferior wine, presumably if there was a shortage of mulberries (page 112). Honey was also added to wine to give it extra sweetness, usually after fermentation. In addition to the use of the berries in the perfume and pharmaceutical industries, blackcurrant leaves used to be dried, ground and added to tea leaves (to save on the greater expense of genuine leaves). And it is not so long ago that dried and ground chicory was added, quite legally, to coffee.

While the blackcurrant has failed to produce any noteworthy 'sports', the same cannot be said of its cousin the redcurrant (*Ribes rubrum*). It has given rise to pink and white variants and there was even mention, long ago, of a yellow specimen. In every other respect, though (including botanically), they are all the same fruit and look very picturesque when the three colours are mixed in a summer pudding with other soft fruits, or simply thrown together in a bowl for dessert. Oddly, whitecurrant varieties appear to be less acidic than red varieties.

The modern redcurrant is the result of breeding work involving three *Ribes* species: *R. rubrum*, *R. vulgare* and *R. petraeum*. They are all found wild in Europe, Central Asia and Siberia, China and Manchuria. *R. rubrum*, which is the most common in Great Britain, occurs naturally as far north as the Arctic Circle and as far south as Scotland and north-

REDCURRANT (*RIBES RUBRUM* (R))

OPPOSITE: The French title to this illustration by Turpin is 'Groseiller à grappes – fruit rouge' ('Bunched redcurrant – red fruit'). There is no varietal name here – fruits often had just the species name but no variety. Only when a number of different variations of the species appeared, or were bred, did varietal names find themselves introduced.

ern England. Any redcurrants found growing in the wild further south are not indigenous, and have usually escaped from cultivated gardens ('garden escapes'). Redcurrants do not appear in any British writings until about the middle of the sixteenth century and the first milestone in their evolution was in 1561, when *R. petraeum* was discovered in a Swiss wood by the famous naturalist Conrad Gesner, who grew bushes in his garden to wide acclaim, on account of the berry size. Around 1620, this species found its way to Great Britain, where (after a hundred years and a certain amount of genetic tinkering) it popped up as the variety 'Prince Albert'. Two other early varieties to rise above the rest were 'Houghton Castle' and 'Raby Castle': these were of excellent quality by any standards and are still grown today.

Early uses of the redcurrant were, again, mainly medicinal. Among other things, they were found to be good for 'hot agues and against hot fires and vomiting'. It's curious how so many fruits in the sixteenth century and thereabouts seemed to be valued for their soothing effect on the insides. One can only guess at the torments people must have suffered, as 'Coolyng the Stomache' seems to have been another virtue of redcurrants. It hardly needs saying that currants were also a popular raw material for wine. Unfortunately, there appear to have been no uses for red and white currants other than those which we know about today, the most popular being redcurrant jelly and summer pudding. Redcurrant jelly, of course, makes the perfect companion for roast lamb, while mint sauce can be, at best, an unnecessary addition (the mint usually floats in a sea of vinegar, often killing the flavour of the lamb).

The last of the *Ribes* fruits is the gooseberry. How it came to have its 'goosegogs' nickname is a mystery but, as is often the case, children were probably behind it. Possibly in response, 'under a gooseberry bush' was a parent's traditional answer to a child's inevitable query regarding the origins of babies. Gooseberries are indigenous to northern Italy, but (as with currants) there is no evidence of them having been grown by the Greeks and Romans. Indeed, the first mention we find of them in England is not until 1275. They occur again early in the sixteenth century, and plants were later imported for King Henry VIII. On both occasions, the bushes came from France, so it is clear that the French were well ahead of the English with regards to fruit cultivation and nursery work. By the end of the sixteenth century, gooseberries were being widely grown in England. Local names soon sprang up for this comparatively new fruit, confirming its success. In Cheshire it was called the 'feaberry'; in Norfolk it was written as 'feabes' but pronounced

BLACKCURRANT (*RIBES NIGRUM*)
OPPOSITE: Usually, blackcurrants are either loved or hated by gardeners – there is the constant battle between the smell of tomcats and the pleasure of eating the berries. Modern varieties are available with much more compact bushes than the older ones, which are especially useful for gardens where space is often at a premium.

'fapes'. Soon, gooseberry and currant plants were being imported from Holland rather than France, as the Dutch gained a reputation for being the best European nurserymen.

The gooseberry went from strength to strength in England during the seventeenth and eighteenth centuries, with gooseberry clubs and societies springing up all over the northwestern counties of Cheshire and Lancashire. Soon, these clubs and their members started to vie with each other for the heaviest berry, and without any doubt its popularity was a form of escapism from often appalling domestic conditions. Poverty and unemployment were rife in much of northern England, especially once the Industrial Revolution started to take effect. Many labourers' cottages in this region had gooseberry bushes, and very soon 'Gooseberry Prize Meetings' were being held, usually in the local public house. The size and weight of the fruit were of paramount importance, and details of varieties and weights were noted in what became *The Manchester Gooseberry Book*. Exactly the same fervour and single-mindedness goes into the cultivation of pot leeks in the northeast of England today. Prizes as high as £10 were offered in the larger clubs for the winning berries. This may not seem much today, but it was a fortune in those days (about ten weeks' wages).

At that time, many new varieties came from Lancashire and Cheshire. Semi-professional growers and cottagers raised their own seedlings in the hope of producing a champion and, if a seedling showed promise by winning competitions, the grower could sell rooted cuttings for as much as £1 each – again, a very useful addition to their income. Some of these early English varieties are still available, while others have gone the way of all flesh. So, sadly, has one of the greatest gooseberry champions of modern times – Albert Dingle of Macclesfield, England died aged 85 while still the record-holder for the heaviest gooseberry. It weighed 37 penny-weight and 15 grains (more than 56g/2oz).

It is said, that one way to increase the size of gooseberries before a show was to place a saucer of water below the bush so that the 'nose' (the flower end of the berry) hangs in the water. The fruit then absorbs water, thus increasing its weight considerably. The skill lies in knowing just how long to leave it in the water: too long, and the berry splits (even explodes), along with the hopes and dreams of the competitor. Gooseberries still have a good following, both for cooking and as a dessert fruit. Varieties range in colour from pale green, to darker greens, yellows, and even shades of red. In England they are commercially grown on a small, specialist scale, but probably just as many are grown in domes-

'SHEBA QUEEN' (*RIBES UVA-CRISPA* VAR. *RECLINATUM*)

OPPOSITE: This variety, formerly called ' Crompton's Sheba Queen', appeared during the heyday of the Northern Gooseberry Clubs. Like many others, it originally bore the name of the raiser, but the 'Crompton's' has since been omitted. On the whole this is a pity, for to do so takes away a piece of personal history.

'VERTE BLANCHE' (*RIBES UVA-CRISPA* VAR. *RECLINATUM*)

RIGHT: Although there is no mention of the fruit by de la Quintinye, this old gooseberry variety certainly seems to have been grown in France for a long time. Very often the remark found under 'varietal descriptions' is 'Variété d'origine très ancienne et inconnue' ('The origin of this variety is old and unknown').

'REYNOLDS' GOLDEN DROP' (*RIBES UVA-CRISPA* VAR. *RECLINATUM*)

OPPOSITE: Reynolds was another private gooseberry enthusiast who turned his hand to breeding new varieties, hoping that a huge berry would make him a fortune. Make no mistake, for there was big money to be made – it may sound trifling today, but in the late nineteenth century £10 was a great deal of money to the working man.

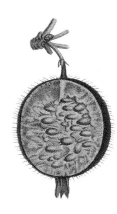

This is the tale of a Cheshire lad
And what a glorious life he had.
By far his greatest claim to fame
Was a record gooseberry to his name.

The world of goosegogs mourned a lot
When Albert died; he was not forgot.
At gatherings of the 'Gooseberry Few'
Not one of them said, 'Albert WHO?'

When that great Gardener in the sky
Said 'Albert, it's your turn to die',
In every place where gardeners mingle,
Tears were shed for Albert Dingle.

So here's a tribute short and plain
So Albert did not die in vain.
May he not lie in a mildewed Hell
But find true peace in Dingle Dell

JOY HARRIS

tic gardens. They are very easy to grow but, like redcurrants, produce their best and most plentiful fruits on side-shoots, growing from a semi-permanent framework of older branches. Many inter-specific hybrids (where one species is crossed with another) exist in the genus *Ribes*; gooseberries and currants both follow that trait. The 'jostaberry' is probably the best-known example and is a hybrid of gooseberry and blackcurrant origin. It has the hybrid vigour that one would expect but, like many other crosses, it has no real virtues. A gooseberry really excels in July, when the true dessert varieties are ripening, and are superb at this time. A good gooseberry wine, chilled on a hot summer's evening, can transport the drinker into another world. Some Loire Valley wines have a hint of gooseberry, making them quite irresistible.

The blueberry is perhaps most strongly associated with the USA. Fresh blueberries are available there from about the last week of May to late July, and are a popular ingredient of muffins, pies and even jelly. During the American Civil War (1861–65), worn-out soldiers drank invigorating beverages containing blueberries to restore their strength after an exhausting day's work. Native Americans used the same fruit to improve the taste of pemmican (a preparation of dried, lean meat; pounded and mixed with fat).

The botanical name of the high-bush blueberry is *Vaccinium corymbosum* and it belongs to the *Ericaceae* family. For many years before, *V. australe* was a better-performing variety, but the two species were then crossed and it is from the resulting hybrids that most varieties and cultivars have arisen. Both species come from the eastern seaboard of the USA. Bushes should not be allowed to carry a crop until two years after planting, which gives them time to establish before they begin fruiting in earnest. The blueberry possesses another virtue in

'GROSSE POURPREE HERISSEE' (*RIBES UVA-CRISPA* VAR. *RECLINATUM*)

OPPOSITE: Here is a gooseberry whose name, when translated from the French, is 'Large, Purple/Crimson and Bristly'. It is interesting to find a title that so descriptively tells the interested reader exactly what the mature berry looks like. Modern varieties tend to be named after people or places – which is not nearly so helpful.

its flowers – in common with many other fruit plants, they are most attractive and here remind one of the shrub *Pieris*.

Blueberries are ericaceous plants and must have extremely acid soil of pH 4.0–5.0 (soil of this nature is usually either peat moorland or just very sandy). In addition, the soil must remain moist. Few places can boast a soil of this type, so the cultivation of blueberries on a commercial scale is a very specialist business. The eastern United States, particularly in the south, has areas with these conditions and the region provides most of the country's blueberries as well as Europe. In Great Britain there is one company in Dorset that grows high-bush blueberries, while Germany has a suitable area in the north of the country, on the Luneburg Heath. Most research connected with the blueberry industry in the USA is carried out at the ARS (Agricultural Research Service) Small Fruits Research Station in Poplarville, Mississippi, where there has been an ongoing breeding programme since the 1970s. Commercial growers in the area cultivate two types of blueberry – the rabbiteye and the southern high-bush, which crops slightly earlier. The rabbiteye is more vigorous, a native of the south and more adaptable to different soil types. It is also drought-tolerant and the fruit has a long shelf life. Varieties cultivated in the United States are not the same as those grown in Europe, but are closely related. The 'European Blueberry' is the bilberry or *V. myrtillus*.

Among the enormous number of species in the *Vaccinium* genus (at least fifty), there are even several distinct cranberries (though what distinguishes them is not clear), including the mountain cranberry (*V. vitis-ideae).* Along with blueberries, many thousands of acres of poor, acidic land in the USA are covered with these assorted berries. They are used for making pies, jams, sauces, preserves, and an enormous number are canned. In a similar way to other genera, such as *Rubus*, *Citrus* and *Ribes*, the different subgenera and species of *Vaccinium* cross with themselves so readily and frequently that their classification was once described by an eminent American botanist (almost underplaying the situation) as 'difficult, contradictory and confusing'.

Raspberries and strawberries are probably neck and neck in popularity as a fruit for growing in the garden. They take up relatively little room, are easy to grow and provide fresh fruit, straight from the plant, from early July (even late June) to November. The raspberry, *Rubus idaeus*, is native to most European countries and the temperate regions of Asia. In common with many other fruits, it is a member of the *Rosaceae* family and is normally found in light woodland and

---

'RED WARRINGTON' (*RIBES UVA-CRISPA* VAR. *RECLINATUM*)

OPPOSITE: Normally listed as just 'Warrington', this is one of scores of gooseberry varieties that were raised by Lancashire cotton-mill workers in an attempt to grow the heaviest fruit. It is still listed today, and has the virtue of staying in good condition on the bush until October, if trained to a north-facing wall.

other shady areas where the mainly surface-growing roots will be kept cool. Raspberries are also found in moorland, and even on chalk downs, where the topsoil is often acidic from the decaying vegetation that has built up over the years. The wild raspberry grows in Asia Minor, notably on Mount Ida, from where it got its specific name of *idaeus*. According to Greek myth, raspberries were originally white until the nymph Ida pricked her finger while picking berries for the infant Jupiter. Since then, raspberries have supposedly been tinged with her blood. As with other fruits, its name has not always been 'raspberry' – the sixteenth-century English writer, John Gerard, called it 'raspis' or 'hindberry'. In Scotland, they are frequently called 'rasps'. This may simply be a contraction, but the 'rasp' part clearly refers to the prickly stems that all varieties had in those days. Thornless cultivars are a modern luxury, not appearing until the 1950s.

Raspberry seeds (which indicate the fruit's use as a food) have been found in settlements dating back as far as the Early Bronze Age. Like many other fruits, they were grown and used by the Greeks and Romans, though more probably for medicinal use rather than for food. 'Stomach troubles' and 'hote burnings' came high on the list of ailments against which raspberries were thought to be efficacious. Raspberry wine has been a popular drink since the Middle Ages, mainly because – we are told rather vaguely – 'it is good for many purposes'. In common with the mulberry and the blackcurrant, raspberries were often added to other drinks to improve their appearance.

Only one raspberry existed in the sixteenth century. Even in the early eighteenth century, there were only the naturally occurring species – a white variant and what was called 'Large Red'. It was not until the nineteenth century that the range of varieties became useful, and by the twentieth century the list was in excess of thirty. The middle years of the twentieth century saw the arrival of a completely new selection of British raspberry varieties. The first were the 'Malling' varieties (after the East Malling Research Station in Kent, where they were bred), such as 'Malling Jewel', 'Malling Promise', 'Malling Leo', 'Malling Delight', 'Malling Admiral' and 'Malling Joy'. Old varieties were examined for desirable characteristics, and completely alien species of *Rubus* were introduced to the breeding programmes. Research then moved from East Malling to the Scottish Crop Research Institute (SCRI). Today, the main area for commercial raspberry growing in Great Britain is just north of Dundee, in Scotland, where the climate is suitable and there are few pests to bother the crop. From here came the 'Glen' varieties, starting with 'Glen Clova', the first good early to appear

'WILMOT'S EARLY RED' (*RIBES UVA-CRISPA* VAR. *RECLINATUM*)

OPPOSITE: If the numerous appearances of his name are anything to go by, Mr John Wilmot (of Isleworth, Middlesex) seems to have been a power in England when it came to breeding new fruit varieties in the early decades of the nineteenth century. However, it appears he was breeding for the 'monster market' here, as this gooseberry is described as large but of second-rate quality.

BILBERRY OR WHORTLEBERRY (*VACCINIUM MYRTILLUS*)

ABOVE: The main difference between the bilberry and the blueberry is the size of the bushes. The bilberry is a great deal smaller and is really more of a clump-forming plant, at 15–45cm (6–18in) tall, whereas the 'High-Bush Blueberry' is 1.2–3.6m (4–12ft) tall. Also, the berries of the bilberry are considerably smaller. They like the same growing conditions, however – strong acidity.

'HIGH-BUSH BLUEBERRY' (*VACCINIUM CORYMBOSUM*)

OPPOSITE: The blueberry is a native of the southern United States and virtually all the fruit sold in Europe still comes from there. This is because there is a relatively small market and they are able to supply it economically. The main requirement for growing blueberries is moist land with a very low pH (that is, highly acidic) – something that is not found elsewhere in large enough areas.

for years. Then came 'Glen Moy' and 'Glen Prosen', the first high-quality, thornless varieties to come on the market. Others followed, the latest two being 'Glen Ample' and 'Glen Magna'.

During this time, a breakthrough occurred with the introduction of 'primocane' varieties, the scientific name for 'autumn-fruiting' varieties. There were already perpetually fruiting raspberries, but these had more disadvantages than advantages. The new primocane varieties were of high quality and they extended the fresh-fruit season from August until the onset of frosts in November. The main objectives of modern raspberry breeding are the same as for every other fruit − good flavour, pest and disease resistance, a lack of thorns, and fruit which is held well out from the canes (stems) to facilitate harvesting. The difference between normal summer-fruiting varieties and autumn ones is quite simple: the canes of summer-fruiting varieties grow in the first year, and carry fruit in the second; those of autumn varieties grow, flower and fruit in the first year. With summer varieties, the fruited canes are cut down straight after fruiting, but with autumn varieties they are left until the following spring. To confuse the two is to court disaster.

In America, the original raspberry varieties did not come from Europe, but from local woods and heaths where they grew wild. However, by the late eighteenth century they were making the journey from Europe, where named varietie were appearing. The two 'races' were hybridized and it was from their progeny that modern American varieties arose, such as 'Meeker' and 'Munger'. No account of raspberries would be complete without the 'Black Raspberry', *R. occidentalis*, of North America. The fruits are unattractively dark but they have several desirable properties, which crossbreeding can transfer to red varieties. The species has been used in breeding programmes for many years, and the canes are around 2.75m (9ft) tall, but armed with vicious thorns. Vegetative propagation is by tip layering, the same method used for blackberries, while the fruits can be large and the crops heavy. 'Black' varieties are still grown and used extensively in the canning and jamming industries, but are almost completely absent from the fresh-fruit market.

In the past, many growers combined raspberry cultivation with strawberries, but a good year for raspberries was not necessarily a good one for strawberries. Consequently, the canneries sometimes faced the problem of having too many raspberries and not enough strawberries. Their clever way around this − however many cans of strawberries they were lacking, a similar number of cans of raspberries were 'accidentally' labelled as strawberries. Not wanting to complain,

BLACKBERRY (*RUBUS FRUTICOSUS*)

OPPOSITE: The blackberry is one of the most widespread wild fruits, and can be found throughout the countryside all over the world. Extensive breeding work has been carried out in the USA, though the results are not necessarily improvements on former or existing varieties. There was a time when size and appearance were all-important, even though the fruit itself was tasteless.

only about one in a thousand customers said anything about the 'mistake'. Most were perfectly happy with the different fruit – an object lesson in consumer response. This was forty years ago, and nowadays any deficit would be made up by foreign imports. Another antic of times past involved the picking gangs, who have since been replaced by mechanical harvesters. In those days, the pickers were paid by weight for what they had gathered. If the raspberries were destined for processing, the quality was immaterial, as the fruit was going to be pulped. For this market, the fruit was picked into buckets, and to get more into the bucket a picker would stir the berries round so that they became a pulp. However, because liquid weighs more than raspberries, it was not unknown for 'foreign' liquid to go into the bucket with the raspberries – and it wasn't always water... which is enough to put anyone off raspberries for life.

The other widely grown species of *Rubus* is *R. fruticosus*, or the blackberry. North America and Europe are the main natural habitats of wild blackberries, which they have a much longer history than raspberries as a semi-domestic fruit. Evidence of blackberries has been found dating to between the last two Ice Ages, and the Romans are known to have eaten them during their occupation of England. Medicines and alcoholic beverages seem to have been the fruit's main destination but very few of those old uses still exist. The chief use to which we now put blackberries is in puddings of every conceivable kind and *au naturel* as a dessert.

The blackberry's early history followed a similar pattern to the raspberry, although the blackberry had two features that delayed its introduction to gardens. The first was its thorns; the second is that there was little point in cultivating what was freely available in the fields and hedges. Furthermore, some of the wild species and hybrids were of such high quality that further crossing was unnecessary. More recently, extensive breeding work has been carried out in the USA, resulting in many new blackberry varieties. Not all are improvements on former or existing ones, and there was a phase when size and appearance were all-important. 'Black Satin', for example, was the most gorgeous-looking blackberry, but it was absolutely tasteless. 'Waldo', on the other hand, has a good flavour and canes of less than 3m (10ft) long.

One of the tricks that nature sometimes plays is to give the most unacceptable varieties a blissful flavour. For example, 'Fantasia' and 'Himalaya Giant' produce canes that are 4.5–6m (15–20ft) long, with thorns like barbed wire. In modern times, one of the most curious blackberries has double flowers. It seems likely that it is not a true blackberry but

BLACKBERRY (*RUBUS FRUTICOSUS*)

OPPOSITE: There is evidence of the existence of blackberries that dates back to between the last two Ice Ages. The Romans ate large quantities during their occupation of England. Medicines, alcoholic beverages and additives to grape wines seem to have been the fruit's chief uses, though these days the blackberry is used predominantly in puddings of all kinds.

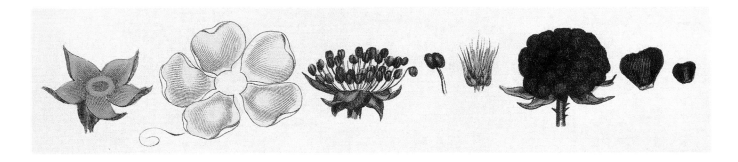

R. ulmifolius 'Bellidiflorus', the double-flowered blackberry. Interestingly, and unlike most plants with double flowers, it does produce fruit, but this fails to exonerate it completely, as they are small, black and inedible. In the 1930s, work was undertaken at Long Ashton Research Station (near Bristol), setting out to find Great Britain's best-flavoured wild blackberry. Candidate plants came in from far and wide and, as luck would have it, a winner was found just before the outbreak of World War II. It survived the war years, and once things had returned to normal it became 'Ashton Cross'. It is still available today and has possibly the best flavour of all.

Inter-specific hybrids are far from rare in the wild and quite common under cultivation. Among the *Rubus* genus, hybrids are extremely numerous. Both professional and amateur plant breeders have produced a bewildering number of crosses, whose quality varies greatly. The loganberry is traditionally regarded as the first 'success' and appeared in 1881, in the garden of Judge Logan in Santa Cruz, California. It is still regarded by many as a cultivated form of the native American blackberry, *R. vitifolius*. Others think it is a sport of that species, with larger, redder and more luscious fruits. Whatever the truth, the popularity of the loganberry increased rapidly, and by 1900 it had crossed the Atlantic, quickly becoming just as popular in Europe. It was easy to grow, it cropped heavily and the unique flavour was universally liked. Soon it was being grown commercially and in gardens on both sides of the Atlantic. However, the loganberry had one important difference from raspberries and blackberries in that it was superb for jams, cooking and other kinds of processing, but was poor for dessert. It is too sharp unless absolutely ripe, and many blackberries share this slight problem. Ripe fruit are too tender and delicate to travel, so it has to be picked while still unripe. The loganberry, although not completely winter-hardy in northern Europe, still wins more often than not when put before tasting panels.

During the 1930s and 1940s, interest in growing hybrid berries flagged when it was found that most stocks were diseased and cropped well below their potential. Although the viruses were subsequently removed, some brand-new varieties were needed. In the 1950s and 1960s, work at the Scottish Crop Research Institute (SCRI) involved *Rubus* species that had not been included in breeding work before, including *R. glaucus*, *R. parviflorus* and *R. ursinus*. The SCRI's first (and most important) offspring, the tayberry, was safely delivered in 1977. At a stroke, the prospective yield of a

BLACKBERRY (*RUBUS FRUTICOSUS*)

ABOVE AND OPPOSITE: North America and Europe are the main natural habitats of wild blackberries, which have a far longer history than raspberries as a semi-domestic fruit. Two features delayed its introduction into gardens – its spiky thorns, and the fact that there was little point in cultivating something that was readily available in the fields and hedges.

Fig. 1.

Fig. 2.

AMERICAN DEWBERRY (*RUBUS CANADENSIS*)

ABOVE: The American dewberry is a more upright version of the blackberry. It is a deciduous shrub with canes up to 2.4m (8ft) tall and is almost completely thornless. The fruits, which appear in the autumn, are black and juicy (though very sour).

EUROPEAN DEWBERRY (*RUBUS CAESIUS*)

OPPOSITE: The dewberry (fig. 2) found in the UK is definitely the poor relation of the blackberry. Its thin and prickly, bluish stems are prostrate, running among grass and other vegetation in wasteland and road verges. The fruits are small, with only a few, large, blue-white drupes.

hybrid cane fruit was doubled without any reduction in quality or deterioration in flavour. And, unlike the loganberry, the tayberry is winter-hardy throughout Great Britain.

Finally, we come to the strawberry. Synonymous with summertime, these are arguably the most important soft fruit, and certainly the ones with the most complicated genetic history. Another member of the prolific *Rosaceae* family, they are indigenous to both northern and southern hemispheres. However, the modern cultivar did not originate in any one place, as several species from different parts of the world were brought together to create the familiar varieties of today. The nearest we can get to a starting point is the Chilean *Fragaria chiloensis*, which has probably played a greater part than any other variety, although some experts favour the most widely distributed species, *F. vesca*. The latter is known as the 'Wood Strawberry', flourishing throughout temperate zones, from northern Europe to the Alpine region. Its small, fragrant fruits have been gathered as a food for centuries, and many see it as the true wild strawberry.

The strawberry's history goes back as far as the Romans, cropping up in the writings of Virgil, Ovid and, later, Pliny. It appears that the fruit was valued for its medicinal properties rather than any culinary merit. By the Middle Ages, the French had begun to transplant *F. vesca* into their gardens, both for eating and for ornamental purposes. Seemingly, the English followed suit and the strawberry was well established by the late fifteenth century. In Shakespeare's *Richard III* (1597), the king makes the following request of the Bishop of Ely: 'When I was last in Holborn, I saw good strawberries in your garden there: I do beseech you send for some of them.' This reference indicates that the bishop was growing strawberries with enough success to attract the attention of writers in the late fifteenth century (when these events actually took place).

The strawberry is also mentioned in the *Grete Herball* (printed by Peter Treueris in 1526), in which it is noted for its medicinal properties. Despite its growing popularity, the normal procedure for growing strawberries was still to transplant from the wild. They would produce fruit the following year or the next one, after which they would be discarded. Ultimately, *F. vesca* merely established the strawberry – it played no part in the fruit's modern development and was grown because it was the only one available. When the superior 'Hautbois' strawberry (*F. elatior*) arrived from mainland Europe, it stole the limelight immediately.

'WILMOT'S SUPERB' (*FRAGARIA*)

OPPOSITE: The 'Wilmot's Superb' strawberry dates from about 1825. Grown in 'extensive plantations' by John Wilmot in his fruit garden in Isleworth, Middlesex, it was an excellent variety, even by the standards of the time, with large fruits. However, it didn't fare so well in America – the heat of summer and the cold winters were just too much for it.

Modern strawberry history really begins in the seventeenth century, following the colonization of the Americas. The Virginian strawberry, *F. virginiana*, was first recorded in Europe in about 1624. Although it was a great improvement on *F. vesca* in size and colour, its flavour was no better than what was already being cultivated. The next crucial development was the arrival in France of the Chilean strawberry, *F. chiloensis*. This was introduced in 1712, and it was this variety, above all others, which really lifted the fruit size, status and usefulness of strawberries in Europe. The 'first-born' of the breeding programmes that followed was *F. ananassa*, an ancestor of most modern varieties.

The next goal was to move beyond the short-season summer varieties (*F. chiloensis*) and the long-season, small-fruited Alpines, without losing the larger fruit size and other benefits of the Chilean variety. Unfortunately, although Alpines and the Chilean variety can be crossed, the seed will be sterile. Then, in late nineteenth-century France, Abbé Thivolet, parish priest of Chenovès, Chalon-sur-Saône, seemed to achieved the impossible. Perhaps with the help of foreign pollen, he produced 'St Joseph', a large-fruited strawberry with a perpetual flowering habit. (which means that the plant will fruit from about midsummer until the cold weather of autumn). 'St Joseph' had achieved this and subsequent perpetuals were called 'remontant' or (more popularly) 'autumn-fruiting' varieties. However, to achieve autumn fruiting with any degree of success, the flowers must be removed up to the end of May. If they are not, the plants exhaust themselves in the early part of the year, and only a few fruit develop in the autumn.

Another Frenchman unravelled the strawberry's genetic peculiarities. Antoine Nicolas Duchesne, father of the modern strawberry, was born in 1747, and had published a botany manual by the time he was 17. In the following year, he noticed that not all strawberry plants were truly bisexual – some carried either male or female flowers, but not both; they were unisexual, and *F. chiloensis* was one such rarity. In early nineteenth-century England, Michael Keen worked tirelessly on crossing *F. chiloensis* and *F. virginiana*. A market gardener from Middlesex, his efforts gave us 'Keen's Imperial' and 'Keen's Seedling', both of which are magnificent. Around the same time, also in England, horticulturist Thomas Andrew Knight produced 'Downton', 'Elton Pine' and 'Elton Seedling', and in the USA the main strawberry pioneers were Nicholas Longworth and Charles M. Hovey. 'Longworth's Prolific' set the scene in 1857, but within a few years 'Hovey's Seedling' was released and swept all before it. Both men had their days of glory.

UNNAMED STRAWBERRY (*FRAGARIA*)

OPPOSITE: The first half of the eighteenth century and the second half of the twentieth were the heydays of strawberry breeding. The older period followed the discovery of the larger South and North American varieties, which led to the large, summer-fruiting ones. The second period, following World War II, was largely a period of great strawberry improvements, which we enjoy today.

SINGLE-LEAFED (*FRAGARIA VESCA MONOPHYLLA*)

ABOVE: The Single-Leafed strawberry (here named 'Fraise à une feuille' by Poiteau) differs from most other strawberries in having 1-foliate leaves as opposed to the usual 3-foliate. It is not an Alpine strawberry, but simply a single-leafed version of the small-fruited, wild strawberry that grows all over northern Europe, including the UK.

CHILEAN (*FRAGARIA CHILOENSIS*)

OPPOSITE: Along with *F. virginiana*, the Chilean strawberry did more than any other species to improve the size of the Old World's varieties and bring them up to the standard that we expect today. European strawberries were small, wild species based mainly on *F. vesca* and its subspecies. The only drawback with *Fragaria chiloensis* was that its plants were either male or female – not bisexual as most others are.

STRAWBERRY VARIETIES FROM
BROOKSHAW'S *POMONA
BRITANNICA* (1812)
LEFT AND OPPOSITE: (left, clockwise
from top left) 'Hoboy', 'Chili' (also
opposite page), 'Scarlet Flesh Pine',
'Scarlet Alpine'. Most of these strawberries
played their part in the development of
the modern fruit. Several 'Pine' varieties
exist: these have a hint of pineapple in
their taste, and 'Cambridge Late Pine' still
wins the votes of the tasting panel fifty
years after its first appearance. It is a
particularly good garden variety.

'FRAISIER DE MONTREUIL' (*FRAGARIA VESCA*)

ABOVE: 'Fraisier du Montreuil' is a very old French selection of *F. vesca*. In the early days of strawberry cultivation, the large, summer-fruiting American species were unknown in Europe, so the two *F. vesca* types (*F. vesca* and *F. vesca semperflorens*, the Alpine strawberry) were grown in gardens. One virtue of these two was that they were ever-bearing rather than just summer-fruiting.

'DOWNTON' (*FRAGARIA VIRGINIANA* ✗ *FRAGARIA CHILOENSIS*)

OPPOSITE: 'Downton' was bred by prolific plant breeder Thomas Andrew Knight, of Downton Castle in Herefordshire. It was one of several of his that made a valuable contribution to the embryonic English strawberry industry. The parentage of 'Downton' is uncertain, but it is most probably a *F. virginiana, F. chiloensis* cross.

Fraisier des bois.

WOOD STRAWBERRY (*FRAGARIA SILVESTRIS*)

ABOVE: In France, this is often called the *Fraisier des Bois* or *Fraise du Bois*. It is the small, wild strawberry of Continental Europe and the British Isles. *Fragaria vesca semperflorens*, a subspecies, is the Alpine strawberry. Neither has played any large part in the evolution of the modern large-fruited strawberry, which has come almost solely from the Americas through species such as *F. chiloensis* and *F. virginiana*.

'BATH SCARLET' (*FRAGARIA VIRGINIANA*)

OPPOSITE: Apart from this excellent illustration by William Hooker (1817), it is difficult to find any hard information on this variety, as the name appears to have died out. But it is most likely to be an English cultivar of *F. virginiana*, first cultivated in Bath, England in the mid-eighteenth century and often called 'Double Scarlet'.

'KEEN'S SEEDLING' (*FRAGARIA*)

ABOVE: In the world of strawberries, 'Keen's Seedling' was certainly one of two or three varieties
that sired the modern strawberry. Bred from 'Keen's Imperial', it was a parent of many other
varieties of exceptional quality. In *Gardener's Magazine* of 1827, 'Keen's Seedling', along with the large
size of the 'Wilmot's Superb', was seen as 'materially alter[ing] the character of the strawberry as a
dessert fruit, and [ranking] it with plums and peaches'.

'WILMOT'S COXCOMB' (*FRAGARIA*)

OPPOSITE: Another of John Wilmot's seedlings, this appeared in 1824 from a cross with his
competitor, Michael Keen's, 'Imperial'. Thus the two great names in strawberry breeding were joined
together. The cockscomb name is derived from the unusual protuberance on the fruit. It is possible
that the true name is 'Wilmot's Coxcombe Scarlet'. Various spellings and combinations of the words
exist, but all refer to the same variety.

'BARNET' (*RUBUS IDAEUS*)

LEFT: The 'Barnet' was given its name by the raiser, Mr Cornwall, of Outer Barnet, London. Other names for it include 'Cornwall's Prolific' and 'Cornwall's Seedling'. It does not compare with 'Red Antwerp' for flavour, but the fruit is larger and the canes are heavier-cropping. Both varieties were still cultivated early in the twentieth century after virtually a hundred years.

RED RASPBERRY
(*RUBUS IDAEUS*)

OPPOSITE: Red raspberries are natives of Great Britain, Europe and many other temperate areas of the world. It was only comparatively recently that the countries where they grew naturally sat up and took notice of them and started to develop new and improved varieties. Differences are found from one country, according to preferences for certain kinds and varieties. The French, for example, list many more autumn-fruiting (primocane) varieties than the summer ones, whereas the United Kingdom lists more summer-varieties.

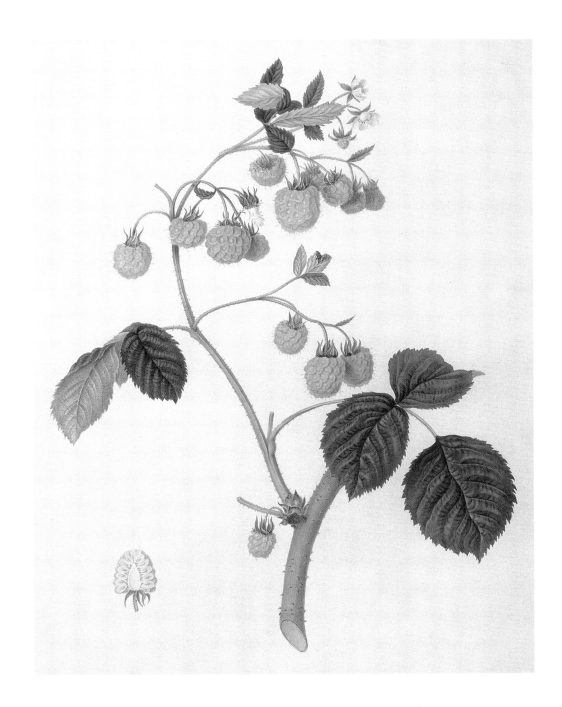

'YELLOW ANTWERP' AND 'RED ANTWERP' (*RUBUS IDAEUS*)

ABOVE AND RIGHT: The 'Yellow' (above) and 'Red Antwerp' (opposite) are actually the same
variety; a third, sweeter variety also exists – the 'Sweet Yellow Antwerp'. Where the same fruit has
been given different names, this usually arises because two people unknowingly raise almost
identical seedlings. Occasionally, two people notice a slight colour change as a result of a mutation –
which isn't as rare as it may seem, because if one individual plant can throw a certain sport, what is
to stop another one from doing so? A third way is for a gardener to steal one of the new plants,
claim it for himself/herself and give it a new name. 'Red Antwerp' certainly existed in 1812, though
it has no connection with Belgium – it was so named because the fruit was similar in size to the
'White Antwerp'. It had an excellent flavour and a long cropping period.

'RED ANTWERP' AND 'WHITE ANTWERP'
(*RUBUS IDAEUS*)

BELOW AND RIGHT: The cultivated raspberry evolved more during the second half of the twentieth century than in all its previous history. Although work had started in the 1930s to improve the varieties of the day, it wasn't until the 1950s that new ones finally became available. Every facet of appearance and physiology came under the microscope, so that by the end of the century pest and disease resistance, thornless canes and autumn fruiting were commonplace.

MYRTLE BERRIES (*MYRTUS COMMUNIS*)

OPPOSITE: Although the common myrtle bush undeniably produces berries, it seems they have such a special taste that most gardeners have yet to be educated with regard to their delights. The berries are normally purple-black in colour, but a strain with white berries exists, as does another that bears variegated leaves.

ELDERBERRY (*SAMBUCUS NIGRA*)

ABOVE: The elderberry is native to North America (*S. canadensis*) and Europe (*S. Nigra*), and has most commonly been used for juice and preserves. However, it does enjoy a certain popularity in the form of elderberry wine. Traditionally, few cultivars were produced as the plant grew so well in the wild, but a small number of superior varieties have been developed for commercial processing – 'Haschberg' from Vienna being the main European cultivar.

CRANBERRY (*VACCINIUM OXYCOCCOS*)

ABOVE AND OPPOSITE: Of the enormous number of species in the *Vaccinium* genus (at least fifty), there are even several distinct cranberries. The mountain cranberry – *Vaccinium vitis idaea* (opposite) is an evergreen shrub, and barely reaches 30cm (12in) in height. It has creeping stems with ascending shoots, and its fruits are small, dark red and edible. The berries are used for pies, tarts, sauces and preserves, and a vast number are canned. The different subgenera and species of *Vaccinium* (as with the *Ribes*, *Citrus* and *Rubus* genera) cross with each other so readily that their classification has proven to be complex and sometimes downright contradictory.

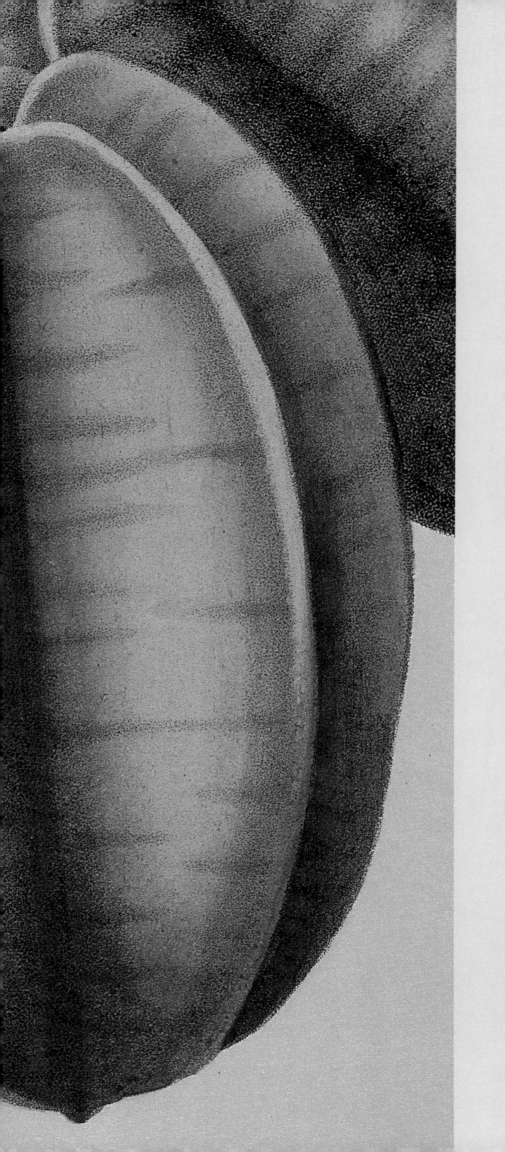

4:Exotic

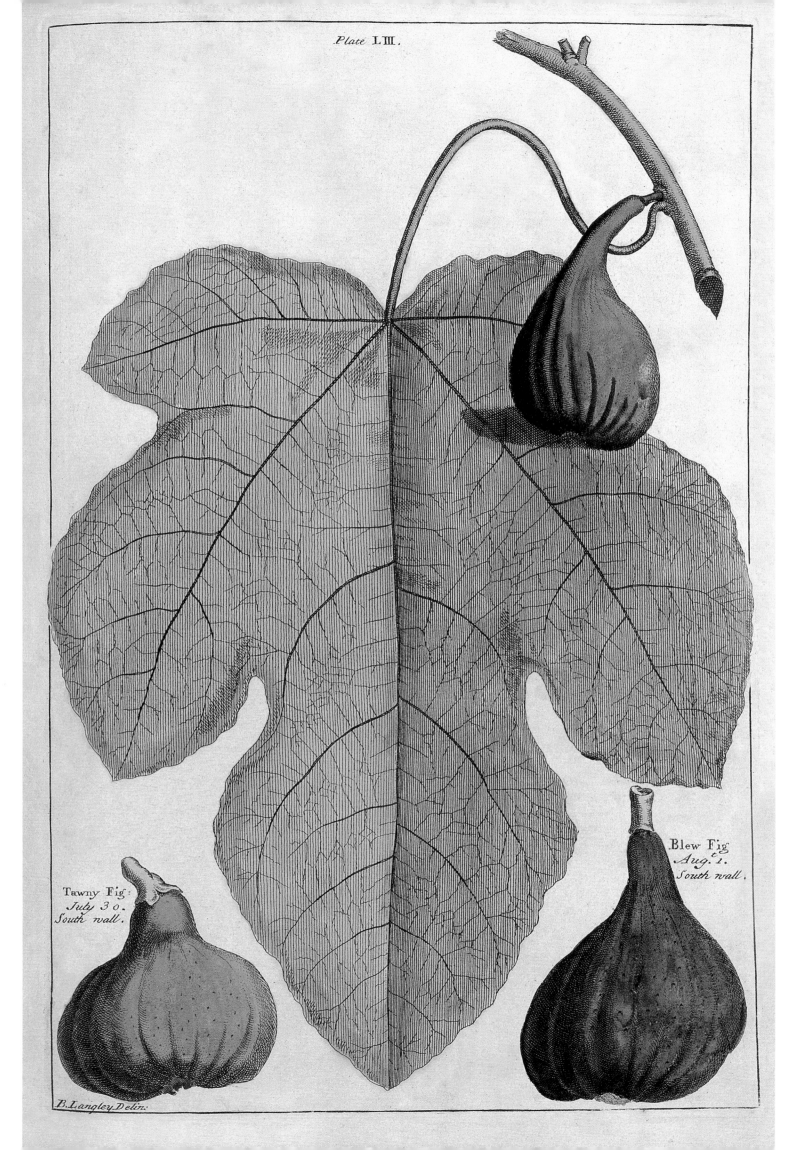

Plate LIII.

Tawny Fig.
July 3 0.
South wall.

Blew Fig.
&
Aug. 1.
South wall.

B. Langley Delin.

Like the mulberry, the fig is a member of the large and diverse *Moraceae* family. Despite its popular association with the Mediterranean region, the fig, *Ficus carica*, originally came from western Asia and the Himalayan region. One of the most ancient cultivated fruits, it spread quickly throughout the known world, carried by the tide of successive civilizations. Biblical references to Adam and Eve 'hiding their nakedness' with fig leaves bears witness to its antiquity. Probably due to its early role in the Garden of Eden, the fig leaf has gone down in history as the traditional upholder of decency and modesty, and countless statues of both men and women are adorned with fig leaves. Another early written account of the fig comes from Egypt and dates from 2700 BC, when a rebellion was apparently quashed by cutting down the rebels' fig trees and vines.

Ancient maritime peoples such as the Phoenicians probably aided the fig's early spread − it was cultivated in Greece as long ago as 900 BC and even earlier in Cyprus. From here, it dispersed throughout the Mediterranean area (in the first century AD, the great Roman encyclopedist Pliny records twenty-nine varieties). The eighth-century Arab conquests revitalized the horticultural importance of the fig in southern Spain and Portugal, and it was from here that it was finally transported to the New World in the sixteenth century, this time accompanied by Christian missionaries. Consequently, the New World was one of the last places to greet the fig, but it did so with open arms. Figs reached California in the mid-eighteenth century, courtesy of a Franciscan mission in San Diego. The variety planted there was later (and rather appropriately) named 'Mission'. In the dying years of the nineteenth century, the United States Department of Agriculture collected plants of over sixty varieties of fig from the Royal Horticultural Society's garden at Chiswick in London. These were shipped to California and, with 'Mission', became the nucleus of a great industry.

The Romans almost certainly brought figs to Great Britain, but it is not altogether clear whether these were plants or dried fruits. One very old variety that is still listed by specialist nurserymen is 'Reculver', which was named after an important Roman port on the north Kent coast. This has a number of synonyms, one of which is 'Franciscana' − which is clearly Italian − and another, interestingly, is 'Mission'. Finally there is 'Gouraud Noir', which is doubtless of French origin. Thomas à Becket, the famous twelfth-century English martyr and Archbishop of Canterbury, was said to have

FIG VARIETIES FROM LANGLEY'S *POMONA* (1729)

OPPOSITE: Black Fig, Blew Fig, Tawny Fig. The fig (*Ficus carica*) is a member of the large and diverse *Moraceae* family, and came originally from western Asia and the Himalayan area. Figs were certainly cultivated in Greece nearly three thousand years ago, and have been famously documented in the biblical Adam and Eve story. They are, in fact, not fruits but flowers, and are essentially inside out, with the true (tiny) flowers grouped within the green outer body. Being on the verge of hardiness, the fig suffers frost damage only very occasionally.

planted fig trees in the garden of the Tarring estate in Sussex. If this story is true, then he must have started one of the oldest 'figgeries' in England, because fig trees are still to be found in the gardens of several houses that have been built over the old estate.

In northern Europe, figs are on the borderline of hardiness. Only very occasionally do they suffer damage from frost and snow, as in the winter of 1999–2000, when in many places the top 10cm (4in) of the young shoots were killed by the cold. These trees carried virtually no crop in 2000 because it is the young 'figlets' in the tips of the shoots that form the following year's crop. In most northern temperate-zone countries, figs behave in an unusual way. The summers are not long or warm enough to allow figs to form, develop and ripen in one growing season, so they have to spread it over two seasons. In year one, the tiny figlets – which are about the size of a match-head – form in the tips of the leafy shoots. Only the top two or three survive the winter and go on to mature as ripe figs in the late summer or early autumn of year two. Almost all young figs of cherry size or larger, which are visible in the spring, will have been killed by the time spring arrives. Only in the warmest gardens will any survive and mature, since the vast majority turn black and drop off in spring or early summer. In warmer countries, or in greenhouses in colder areas, figs will produce two (possibly even three) crops a year.

Figs reproduce in a very odd way. For a start, they are actually not fruits at all, but flowers, and the most bizarre thing about them is that they are inside out – the true flowers are tiny and clustered together inside the green outer body. To see them, the fig must be cut open, and each flower is either male or female. If this sounds rather far-fetched, then what follows is even more extraordinary. Imagine a fig tree, in Italy, where it produces as many as three crops a year. In the autumn, a very specialized little fly called the fig wasp enters the semi-formed figs through a tiny hole in the blunt end of the fruit. It lives there all winter, only emerging in the spring, by which time the new spring figs have appeared on the trees. On leaving their winter home, the wasps enter these new and smaller fruitlets and, once inside, the wasp lays its eggs and then dies. The wasp eggs hatch when the tiny internal flowers open, and the young wasps (covered in pollen) leave the fig. The wasps then enter other figs and automatically pollinate the tiny flowers. On departure from these, they discover that it is autumn again and it is getting cooler, so they wisely decide to stay put

'BROGIOTTO NERO' (*FICUS CARICA*)

OPPOSITE: Italy is one of the principal homes of the fig, so it is to be expected that she is represented here. In fact, the fig has been associated with Italy since at least 400 BC, when one stood in front of the Temple of Saturn, in Rome. This unfortunate tree had to be removed because it was 'upsetting' a statue (presumably, tipping it over).

FIG 209

Fico Fetifero, o Fico dell' Osso

Domenica Del Pino disegnò in Finale 1826

Giuseppe Pera inc. in Firenze

FIG 211

until spring. And this is where we come full circle. In colder countries, such as Great Britain, there are no fig wasps. However, this is unimportant – pollination and fertilization are unnecessary, and the figs simply keep on growing until they reach maturity.

There are many different uses of figs. Unfortunately, they are usually first encountered as little brown bricks of dried and pressed fruit, wrapped in cellophane, and eaten around Christmas time. This is a sad end for such a noble and ancient fruit, for the way to experience the fig at its most delicious is to catch it, in its Mediterranean home, just as it falls from a tree. If they are allowed to fall to the ground, the ripest ones will burst open, and these are the best of all. Figs can also be encountered in a dark-brown, sweet and sticky fluid whose origin remains something of a mystery – syrup of figs. The fig's medicinal properties have been prized since the time of the pharaohs, but remains as nothing when compared to the pleasures that can be derived from consuming a deliciously ripe specimen.

Unlike the fig, the kiwi fruit is a relative newcomer to most of the world, and has only recently taken on its 'kiwi' name. *Actinidia chinensis,* is a member of the family *Actinidiaceae*. (In 1986 its name was changed to *A. deliciosa* in order to give a different species name to the smooth-skinned and hairy-skinned fruits – the smooth-skinned fruit remained *A. chinensis*.) It has several common names: in its native country of China, it is the 'strawberry peach', while the rest of the world knew it originally as the 'Chinese gooseberry'. With its unusual, furry brown skin and beautifully patterned interior, it is extremely appealing to the eye. Its bright-green flesh and rows of dark pips are the saviour of the artistic cook, while the flavour is fresh and pleasant, without the brashness and strength of many other fruits. Importantly, a single fruit contains the same amount of vitamin C as ten lemons.

Kiwi fruits have been a minor crop for about three hundred years and are still gathered from the wild, especially in Hupeh province in China, and it wasn't until the mid-nineteenth century that the fruits were even seen by Western explorers. Ernest Wilson was the first to collect seeds: he brought them back to London, then sowed them, and the resulting plants flowered in 1909. The fruit and its seeds were introduced to New Zealand in 1906 and quickly became a major export. At this point it was felt that a more marketable name was required (so it became the 'kiwi fruit') and the plants first fruited in 1910. Commercial production started in about 1930, when trials were carried out and selec-

---

'FETIFERO' (*FICUS CARICA*)

OPPOSITE: 'Human' pictures are particularly interesting because something of the artist's character comes through in the painting. Clearly Gallesio has a fig tree at home whose fruit is being attacked by birds and he is passing this warning onto other gardeners. Note also that the fig is perfect and has just split with ripeness.

'BORDEAUX' (*FICUS CARICA*)

OPPOSITE: The 'Bordeaux' is an old French fig though is not mentioned by de la Quintinye. It is large, long and very dark (even black) when it is ripe. When it cracks along its length, this is the signal you have been waiting for – it means that the fruit is perfect for eating.

WHITE FIG (*FICUS CARICA*)

ABOVE: Fortunately, we know that the 'White Fig' is another name for the excellent 'White Marseilles', also known as 'White Naples'. Its fame even reached the United States in the nineteenth century, where it was found to be 'better than "Brown Turkey" [still a popular variety] under glass, but not as good outside'.

FICUS CARICA VERDECCHIUS. Aldrov.

FIG 215

tions made. By 1940, production of kiwi fruits was well established. In 1953, an export drive began; until then, the fruit had been sold largely at home. By the late 1980s, an incredible ninety-nine per cent of world production was coming from New Zealand, and ninety-five per cent of that was grown in the Bay of Plenty area.

The kiwi reached California in the early 1900s. By 1984, there were 2400 hectares (6000 acres) being grown. One plant dating from 1935 was still alive in 1982 and producing 180kg (400lb) of fruit annually. However, by 1983, Italy was the world's third largest producer, half of which was exported. An important feature of *A. deliciosa* is that the plants are single-sexed – male or female. Male plants have to be planted with the females in order for fruit to be produced, and a ratio of one male to five females is usual. 'Hayward' is the most widely grown female variety and 'Tomai' the most popular male variety.

There is an *Actinidia* from the Far East called *A. arguta* (the Tara vine or Kokuwa), which made a name for itself by producing a bisexual 'child'. This offspring is now available as 'Issai'. The fruits are smaller and smooth-skinned, but 'Issai' is a great deal hardier than its more commercial relations and has enabled the cultivation of single kiwi plants in cooler northern climates. Another bisexual variety, 'Jenny', is also available, while a more ornamental relation, *A. polygama* 'Silver Line', has small, yellow and bitter fruits, which are sometimes salted and eaten in Japan. Other parts of the plant are rich in an oil that lures and intoxicates cats – much like catnip. More controversially, the same oil is used to tame lions and tigers in captivity.

The genus *Citrus* of the family *Rutaceae* is so vast, and its origins so clouded, that a page or so can only scratch the surface. This can only be a thumbnail sketch of the citrus family but it serves to illustrate its immense magnitude, diversity and importance. The genus includes such familiar fruits as the orange, lemon, lime, grapefruit and mandarin. Today's *Citrus* fruits probably arose from about a dozen wild species that originated in the region encompassing Southeast Asia and India. It is probable that Arab traders in Asia brought *Citrus* plants back to the Middle East, from where they spread to Europe through a combination of the Arab conquests and, later, the Crusades. Portuguese navigators are thought to have introduced superior varieties from Southeast Asia in the sixteenth century. Along with the Spanish, Portuguese explorers also introduced *Citrus* plants to the New World in the sixteenth century.

'VERDINO' (*FICUS CARICA VERDECCHIUS*)
OPPOSITE: Clearly another Italian fig, and not surprisingly (most mature figs are green) named after its colour (*Verdino* means 'greenish' or 'pale green'). Although Italy still has a strong association with the fig, surprisingly forty percent of modern fig cultivation takes place in Turkey, not Italy – perhaps not so surprising bearing in mind that modern Turkey was once part of the Roman Empire.

Over the centuries, *Citrus* species have been selected, crossed, improved and re-crossed so many times that the relationships between them border on the incestuous. Depending on where it is growing, the same variety will vary in size, colour and taste. The commercial growth of citrus fruits extends around the world in a wide belt, lying roughly between the fortieth parallels north and south. With the expansion of modern storage and transport systems, a network of trade routes, similar to the old silk routes, has built up, and now reaches all parts of the world where citrus fruits are eaten. There are around two thousand varieties of *Citrus*, of which about a hundred are grown on a large scale, making it the most widely grown tree fruit in the world.

Closely related to oranges, mandarin varieties (*C. reticulata*) include the true mandarins, clementines, satsumas and tangerines, and are favoured for their sweetness and the fact that they are easy to peel. We have the USA to thank for the delicious range of grapefruits (*C. x paradisi*) now available – they have improved immeasurably, being much sweeter and available in pink or even red hues, and there is also one with green skin. The USA produces about ninety-five per cent of the world's grapefruits. The name 'grapefruit' probably arises from a very old variety (long since vanished), whose fruit hung from the trees like bunches of grapes.

There are innumerable other citrus fruits available today. The uniquely named Ugli (*C. reticulata*) is possibly a hybrid of a tangerine, a grapefruit and a Seville orange, while the shaddock (*C. maxima*) is native to Malaysia and an ancestor of the grapefruit. The shaddock is an 'industrial' *Citrus* and an important ingredient in the production of jam and fruit syrup. The pomelo (*C. maxima*) comes from Israel and is a cross between a shaddock and a grapefruit. To these can be added a number of other oddities, like the ortanique and the malaquina. The sambal (*C. amblycarpa*) is small but odd in the extreme. It is green, even when ripe, and so gnarled and wrinkled as to have no real shape. The flesh is also greenish. *C. aurantifolia* is the lime, whose oil is used in the perfume industry – its juice goes in soft drinks.

The Seville orange (*C. aurantium*) is mainly used for marmalade, but is also an ingredient of Cointreau. *C. sinensis* is as close as it is possible to get to the true orange: it has about two hundred varieties, such as the navel orange and the blood orange, but the most important and plentiful is 'Valencia'. *C. limon* is the botanical name of the lemon, and has many varieties. *C. medica* is the Citron and is used for making candied peel. *C. medica* var. *sarcodactylus*, the 'Buddha's

'VERDONE ROMANO' (*FICUS CARICA*)

OPPOSITE: This extremely popular variety, still grown today, is perhaps better known as 'White Adriatic'. It is another mouth-watering example of an Italian fig at the peak of perfection, as shown by it starting to split. To eat a fig at its very best, two things are absolutely vital: it must be on the point of (if not actually) splitting, and it must be warm (which the sun does better than anything else).

Hand' or 'Buddha's Fingers' Citron, is a strong contender for the weirdest fruit of all. This is divided into around ten independent sections that hang down, looking bizarrely like fingers. Close to the genus *Citrus*, but separate from it, are the tiny golden-orange kumquats (*Fortunella* spp.), the 'Casimiroa' or 'Mexican Apple' (*Casimirea edulis*) and the 'Wampee' (*Clausenia lansium*).

Of all the fruit in this book, the melon is the only true annual. It is sown, grows into a plant, flowers, fruits and then dies, all within a year. Melons (*Cucumis melo*) and watermelons (*Citrullus lanatus*) are part of the large family *Cucurbitaceae* – others include cucumbers, luffas, marrows and courgettes, gherkins, pumpkins and the wild European plant white bryony. Most are climbing or trailing plants and produce heavy fruits, which are about ninety per cent water. The first melon-like plant may have come from Central Asia or Africa – there are arguments for both. They were cultivated by the Greeks and Romans alike, while it is believed that Pope Paul II died in 1471 (after eating too many of them). Melons are grown all over the tropical and subtropical world, and also – though not commercially – under glass in temperate countries. Continual crossbreeding has led to a great many new species, varieties and cultivars.

Melons divide into four groups: Cantaloupe, Net, Ogen and Winter melons. The 'Cantaloupes' are named after Cantalupa, a small town near Romo. They are generally round or slightly flattened. Nearly all are clearly divided into segments on the surface and the skin is sometimes warty and uneven. The orange flesh is mouth-watering, and are the finest-flavoured melons. As they do not keep very long after cutting, they are left on the plants until almost ripe and should then be eaten as soon as possible. The French variety 'Charantais' is an excellent example of a Cantaloupe. 'Net' melons get their name from the net-like pattern on the skin surface. Their flesh is an appetizing apricot colour and they taste somewhat like the Cantaloupe, though slightly less well defined. 'Galia' is a good and typical variety.

'Ogen' melons are named after the kibbutz in Israel where they were first grown. The skin is dark green, with orange banded markings that divide the surface into segments. The flesh is pale green and has a superb flavour. When ripe, these melons have a lovely scent and are soft at the flower end. Lastly, there are 'Winter melons' better known as

CITRUS VARIETIES (*CITRUS SINENSIS* –ORANGE, *CITRUS MEDICA* – CITRON, *CITRUS LIMON* – LEMON)
OPPOSITE: 1. *Orange nain à feuilles de myrthe* (Myrtle-Leaved Small Orange), 2. *Limon à fruit doux* (Sweet-Fruited Lemon), 3. Citron, 4. *Pomme d'orange dite Geroof de Oragnie appel* (not a real orange!). There are around two thousand varieties of *Citrus*, a hundred of which are grown on a large scale. The *Citrus* genus includes such familiar fruits as the orange and lemon, as well as the mandarin, lime, grapefruit and more obscure fruits such as the shaddock or the pomelo. *Citrus* species have been crossed and re-crossed so many times over the centuries that they have become the most widely grown tree fruit in the world.

'LIMONIER MELLAROSE' AND 'BIGNETTE' (*Citrus limon*)

ABOVE & OPPOSITE: Most of the old lemon varieties like 'Limonier
mellarose' (above) and 'Bignette' (opposite) are now in what we might call
'living museums', forming a gene bank for the future. No variety of lemon is
without its virtues and they may be needed again for future cultivation. In this
way, hopefully, none of the old characteristics are lost.

'Honeydew'. They are dark green or yellow, and their flesh is pale green or almost white. The least tasty of the four groups, they are sweet and refreshing. Their shape is elongated, like a rugby ball. Honeydews are late-ripening, their skin hard and grooved, and they have good keeping qualities. In Great Britain, large quantities are imported from Spain. Melons are quite simple to grow in temperate countries, though they do need the protection of a greenhouse or frame.

Watermelons (*Citrullus lanatus*) are a completely different fruit, with none of the dessert qualities of the others. They are relatively tasteless, a quality that breeders are trying to correct, but they are superb for quenching thirst on a hot day. Watermelons originated in North Africa and India and are grown throughout the Tropics. Widely exported, they can grow to a huge size – 20kg (45lb) and more. The flesh of a watermelon is pink to red and strangely crisp, a feature that adds to its attraction and thirst-quenching properties. The flesh is filled with dark seeds, which are roasted in some countries and sold, salted, like nuts. The best guide to the ripeness of a watermelon is to tap it as though knocking on a door. The duller the sound, the safer it is to go in – if it is almost metallic, it is not ready. The main watermelon exporters are the Mediterranean countries, the southern United States and Mexico.

One of the most exotic fruits in the mind of those living in cooler climates has to be the pineapple. *Ananas comosus,* of the family *Bromeliaceae,* conjures up romantic pictures of desert islands. In fact, the pineapple is a native of southern Brazil and Paraguay, where its wild ancestors still grow and flourish. Long before Europeans set foot in the New World, it was domesticated by natives, who carried it north to Mexico and the West Indies. Christopher Columbus first saw pineapples in Guadeloupe in 1493 and then in Panama in 1502.

The Bahamas have been producing pineapples for more than 250 years. Interestingly, Bahamians used to place pineapples and their tops outside their homes as a sign of welcome and friendship. This gave rise to the habit of many of the great houses of Europe having stone pineapples placed on the top of their gate pillars – a few of the originals still exist.

Pineapples spread to the Pacific islands and West Africa in the sixteenth century. They arrived in China in 1594 but only reached Europe in the early eighteenth century. By the end of the century they were flourishing in France and England, lovingly cultivated in the hothouses of the great country houses, where there was great competition to grow the best or largest number of pineapples. (In fact, one of my ancestors was one of the first people to grow a pineapple

'POMO D'ADAMO CEDRATO' (*CITRUS MEDICA*)

OPPOSITE: *Citrus medica* is the Citron. They can weigh up to 1.5kg (4lb) and originally came from Southeast Asia. Although they look like large lemons, they are not as juicy yet are sweeter. Their main modern use is for making candied peel from the thick pith beneath the skin. They are mainly grown commercially in Italy, Greece, India and the United States.

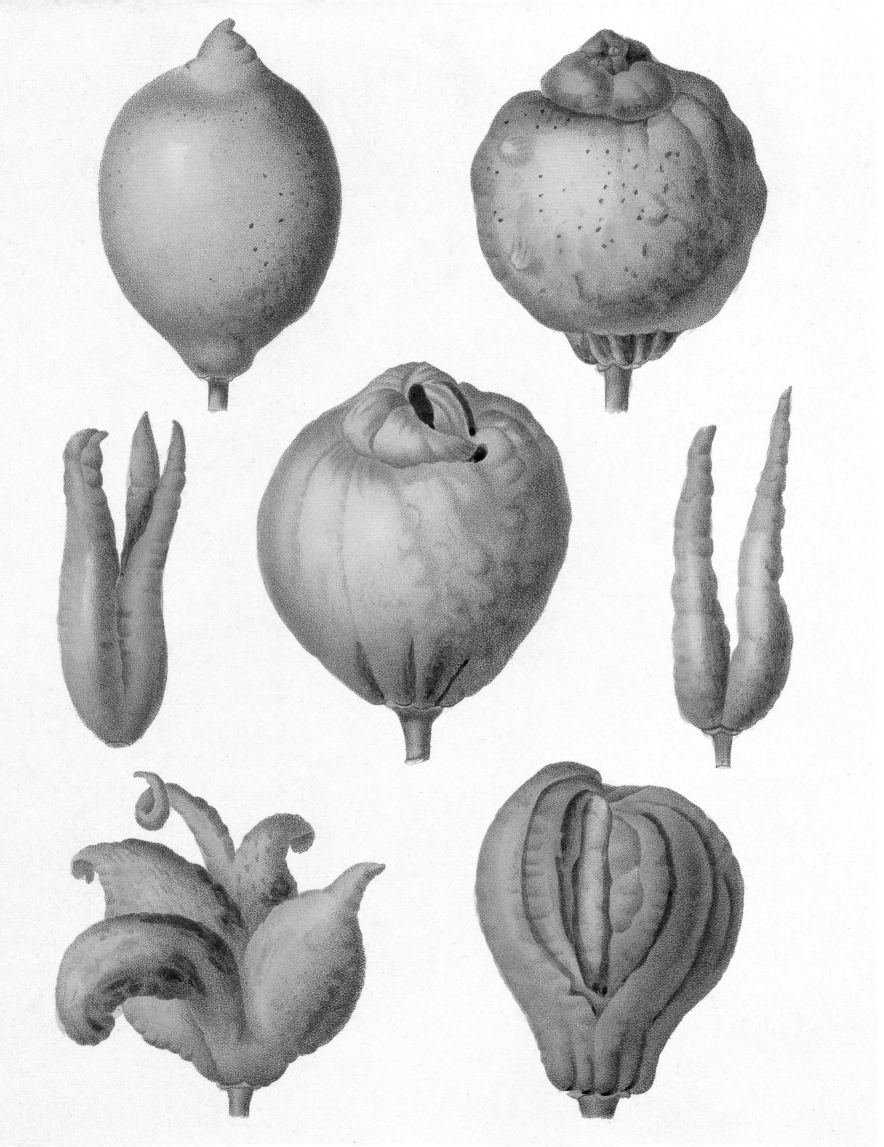

in Great Britain.) Pineapples have been grown in Florida since 1860 and are one of the main, commercial, tropical fruits. Available fresh, in season, or chopped up and canned, all year round, its juice makes a superb chilled drink on a hot summer's day. Additionally, pineapples contain an enzyme called bromelin, which breaks down protein. A tough piece of stewing or grilling steak may be rubbed with a pineapple slice or marinated overnight, and this will tenderize the meat as well as probably improving its flavour.

The word 'pineapple' has two sources. Its French name, *ananas*, comes from the Indian name *nana ment*, or 'exquisite fruit'. Columbus thought the fruit looked like a fir cone so he called it *'pina'*, which over the course of time became 'pineapple'. Their flowering and fruiting is a fascinating process. When a plant is between one and two years old, it sends up a central stem for flowering, which then thickens near the top and develops into a flower-head. The individual flowers (a hundred or more per head) are purple or reddish, each with a yellowish or green bract, depending on the variety. The head continues to grow, producing a compact tuft of stiff, short leaves on top. After a while, each flower produces a small fruit. These fuse together into a compound 'false' fruit, which grows into a juicy and fleshy pineapple measuring around 30cm (12in) in height. The scales on the outside are the remains of the flowers, and pollination is carried out by hummingbirds. However, pollination is unnecessary and undesirable for fruit formation, as the resulting seeds are small and hard.

Pineapples are propagated vegetatively using the crowns, side-shoots or suckers. Improvements − especially with regards to shelf life − are always being sought. As pineapples must be left on the plant to ripen, they have to be cut and moved quickly, and air transport is the only feasible means of transport. The flavour of a pineapple varies with the variety, and its scales are important markers of quality. The more naturally bumpy and pockmarked the surface, the better the flavour. The less marked, the weaker the taste, but the juicier and sweeter the flesh. Ripeness is indicated when the tips of the scales turn brown, while the fruit will be softer at the end that lacks leaves.

Bananas are now so much a part of everyday life that it is hard to imagine a world without them. They are one of the most convenient fruits to eat − just peel off the yellow wrapping and there lies the pristine edible part. 'Banana' is really a portmanteau word describing a multitude of species, varieties and cultivars, some edible, others purely

BUDDHA'S HAND OR BUDDHA'S FINGERS (*CITRUS MEDICA* VAR. *SARCODACTYLUS*)
OPPOSITE: This citron has to be one of the strangest fruits in the world − of any genus. Each fruit is split into ten or so finger-like sections, which gives the impression of a hand. The fruit is in great demand in the Far East for its fragrance, and is also grown for its ornamental and curiosity value.

ornamental. They are members of the *Musaceae* family and their usually accepted botanical name is *Musa acuminata*. There are two main types of banana – those that can be eaten raw as dessert (bananas), and those which need to be treated or processed in some way to make them palatable and digestible (plantains). Apple bananas and rice bananas are plantains, while 'Cavendish' and 'Gros Michel' are both varieties of dessert banana.

Bananas probably originated in Southeast Asia, as far south as northern Australia. The Greeks and Romans knew of them as early as the third century BC, but they were not seen in Europe until the tenth century AD. They spread to the New World when Portuguese sailors took plants from West Africa to South America, and are now the world's fourth largest fruit crop, after grapes, citrus and apples. Bananas are grown throughout the world's tropical and subtropical regions, and most of those reaching Europe are from South and Central American countries, the West Indies and Africa. Only plantains are now imported from Southeast Asia.

A banana plant is large and has a trunk composed entirely of leaf stalks rolled up together. The leaf blades are 2–3m (6–10ft) long and the trunk of rolled-up leaves is a similar height. The structure of the leaves is fascinating. Both the leaf stalks and the midrib have an internal structure similar in effect to an internal beam in a modern building – large air spaces and a succession of crisscrossing struts. The leaf blade consists of a strong midrib with hundreds of close, parallel veins extending to the leaf edge. Each of the veins is straight and unbranched, so that the leaf is very strong from the midrib to the edge but comparatively weak between the veins. Thus, the whole plant is built to withstand hurricanes without suffering any serious damage. The leaf stalks, the trunk and the midrib can bend without breaking and the leaf blade is such that it will tear quite easily from midrib to edge and become tattered, yet the veins and other conducting tissues will emerge unscathed. After the storm, the plant returns to business as usual.

After a banana plant has fruited, it is cut down to the ground, but not before a sucker has started to grow from its base. If it is not cut down, it will die because its fruiting work is done – each stem only fruits once. The bananas grow on stems that grow out from the trunk. Each stem produces upwards of ten 'hands' or bunches, each carrying twelve to sixteen 'fingers' (bananas). A single stem will therefore produce between one hundred and two hundred bananas, which are harvested when bright green and unripe, as they ripen from their green state better than any other fruit.

LIME (*CITRUS AURANTIFOLIA*)

OPPOSITE: Although one always thinks of limes as being green, it is really only the ones that we see in bars that are this colour. The remainder are greeny-yellow, or plain yellow when ripe. There are two main varieties, 'Mexican' and 'Bears'. Their uses are similar to those of the lemon – they are generally too acidic for anything except flavouring.

'Inside the fruit is a cavity more or less filled with an aromatic mass of double-walled membranous sacs filled with orange coloured, pulpy juice and as many as 250 small, dark-brown or black, pitted seeds' – so runs a botanist's description of the fruit of *Passiflora edulis*, the passionfruit or purple granadilla'. Passionfruits owe their name to the structure of their flowers, for the number of stigmas, stamens, crown leaves and sepals reminded early Spanish missionaries of Christ's Passion. When the Spaniards first saw the flowers in the jungle, they looked upon them as divine inspiration. It gave them a useful hook on which to hang some very good reasons why the Native Americans should embrace the Christian faith. And if this method did not meet with success, then they were all soon persuaded by other, less horticultural methods.

Passionfruits are members of the family *Passifloraceae*, whose primary genus is *Passiflora*. The hardy passionflower that we grow in gardens is *P. caerulea*. Its fruit, although it hardly warrants the name, is yellow to orange when ripe, and is edible but unappetizing. *P. edulis*, the main edible passionfruit, is a vigorous, woody climber from the Amazon rainforest of Brazil, Paraguay and northern Argentina. It exists in two forms – the purple-fruited variety is the most well-known, while the other has yellow fruits. Brazil has a long-established passionfruit industry, with canning and juice extraction factories. The better-known purple passionfruit is the preferred dessert variety, and the yellow passionfruit is predominantly used for its juice.

Before 1900, on the other side of the world, passionfruits became naturalized in Queensland, Australia. However, disaster occurred in 1943, when crops were struck by the parasitic root fungus, *Fusarium*. It killed most of the purple-fruited plants but not the yellow ones, which led to the practice of grafting scions of the purple form onto seedling rootstocks raised from the yellow fruits. These were also resistant to harmful eelworms. Another passionfruit, the giant granadilla' (*P. quadrangularis*), is occasionally seen in shops, as is the banana passionfruit' (*P. mollissima*). If *granadilla* sounds Spanish, then it is no accident, for when the Spanish conquistadors saw the fruit, they were immediately reminded of the pomegranate. *Granadilla* means 'little pomegranate'. A perfect passionfruit will have dark-purple, smooth or wrinkled skin. The fruit is cut in half and the inside is scooped out, and when chilled, togther with a few drops of lemon, it could be set before a king.

'INDIAN LIME' (*CITRUS AURANTIFOLIA*)

OPPOSITE: The 'Indian Lime' is in fact a 'sweet lime', also known as the 'Palestine Lime' or (within India) as 'Mitha Limbu' (*Mitha* means 'sweet'). It is not only used as a flavouring, but can also be eaten raw as a fruit, and is valued for its cooling properties when used to treat fevers or jaundice.

PINK GRAPEFRUIT (CITRUS X PARADISI)

ABOVE: This has long been a popular dessert fruit, but its
popularity took off in the late twentieth century with the
arrival of the red-fleshed varieties and exra promotional activity.
It may have originally come as a mutant or sport from a
Southeast Asian shaddock, and is now commercially grown in
Spain, Cyprus, Israel, Egypt, South Africa, United States and
Central America.

SHADDOCK (CITRUS MAXIMA)

OPPOSITE: The main claim to fame of the shaddock is that it
is the parent of the far superior grapefruit. It is a much larger
fruit and can weigh up to about 5kg (11lb). The skin is very
thick and loosely attached to the flesh, which is greenish-yellow
to red. The shaddock is not a dessert fruit; instead, its flesh is
either candied or made into jam.

Pompelmouse ordinaire.

The grapevine, *Vitis vinifera*, belongs in the family *Vitaceae*. There are almost 450 species in the family, but only one has commanded great attention for thousands of years, and today grapes are the most widely grown fruit in the world. The importance of grapes can perhaps be best judged by observing what happens to them after they have been picked: five per cent are turned into grape juice; another five per cent are dried to produce currants, sultanas and raisins; ten per cent are eaten fresh in desserts; whereas eighty per cent are fermented and then bottled as wine, brandy, Cognac, Armagnac and a host of other drinks.

Grapes probably originated in the Black Sea area, and excavations certainly indicate that they were first domesticated in that region. The cultivation of grapes is noted in the book of Genesis, which gives a fair idea of the immense antiquity of grapes and vineyards. Noah and King Solomon both had vineyards, while the Egyptians are known to have made wine from grapes some five or six thousand years ago. Everyone held the grape in high esteem, probably as much for the wine as for the fruit. The Romans promoted Bacchus to the status of a god for having taught Man the purpose of grapes. Bacchus is often represented as an old man, crowned with a garland of grapes and vine leaves to show us that 'wine taken immoderately will turn us childish like old men', and one cannot argue with that. The Greek philosopher Plato had very definite views on wine. He firmly believed that 'nothing more excellent or valuable was ever granted by God to Man'. Edward Bunyard – the great English nurseryman, wine connoisseur and *bon viveur* – would almost certainly have been in agreement there.

The cultivation of grapes in ancient times was clearly of a very high standard. A variety that was grown in Damascus produced bunches weighing anything up to 12kg (25lb). Another vine supposedly bore grapes as large as pigeon eggs, and in the islands of the Archipelago single bunches were each said to have weighed between 4.5kg and 18kg (10–40lb). Some Persian grapes were apparently so large that a single berry made a good mouthful. Vines like that no longer exist, although perhaps it was only fermented grape juice that created them in the first place.

Bearing in mind how long it is since grapes were first used to make wine (five to six thousand years), however, they took a long time to reach Europe. We find no mention of them until about 1500 BC; then, Greek colonists started growing grapes near Marseilles in southern France. From there, the grapes started their journey north with the Roman

PURPLE SEVILLE ORANGE (*CITRUS AURANTIUM*)

OPPOSITE: Bearing in mind the ornamental value of the true Seville orange, the purple version (if it still exists) should be a show stopper. However, the usual use for 'sour' ('Seville') oranges, for the production of marmalade would, presumably be excluded – since purple marmalade just might take some getting used to.

armies, until they had penetrated practically every corner of Europe. Indeed, Italian wine was so prized that a slave could have been exchanged for a single jar. Excavated wine amphorae from Richborough, Kent carried labels that showed that the wine inside had come from the slopes of Mount Vesuvius before the catastrophic eruption in AD 79.

The first written evidence of grape cultivation in England is in a book written in AD 731 by the illustrious monk, the Venerable Bede. The number of vines being grown around Ely in Cambridgeshire was such that the Isle of Ely was unofficially renamed 'The Isle of Vines'. 'Wine is not for the young but for the old and wise,' said Aelfric, the English Benedictine Abbot, in about AD 1000.

In the New World, grapes got off to a slow start. Settlers in New England initially grew European varieties, but these were a failure so they turned their attention to native North American vines of a completely different species, *Vitis labrusca*, or the 'Fox Grape'. These fared much better and, in addition, were resistant to vine mildew, a devastating fungus of European varieties. They also appeared to be free of *Phylloxera*, the extremely serious gall-forming root aphid that can decimate European varieties. During the nineteenth century, *Phylloxera* was rampant in Europe and seedlings of the 'Fox Grape' were sent over for use as rootstocks for the European varieties.

On the other side of the coin there are dessert (or table) grapes. These are grown in most of the same countries as wine grapes, and the main difference lies simply in the varieties. Whereas many of the dessert varieties can also be used to make wine, the wine varieties make poor table grapes, as few are sweet enough. In the more northern countries, wine grapes are more successful outdoors than table grapes. Nevertheless, there are a small number of dessert varieties that grow quite well, notably 'Black Hamburgh'. In these colder countries, table grapes are nearly always grown in greenhouses, where they fare extremely well if properly cared for. Grapes are still generally described as either 'black' or 'white', although many of the newer varieties are shades of pink and red – this is especially so with North American varieties. One grape that seems to be quite happy outdoors in the British Isles is the American 'strawberry' grape, and perhaps the last word on grapes (and the 'strawberry' grape in particular) should be left to Edward Bunyard. In 1927, he said that 'The Strawberry Grape is beloved by some but, to me the flavour suggests a cross between a tomcat and a black currant and it is, to most palates, undesirable and, happily, rare.'

SEVILLE ORANGE (*CITRUS AURANTIUM*)
OPPOSITE: The largest quantities of commercial Seville or 'sour' oranges are produced in Spain. Many of them are shipped to the UK for making marmalade. Oddly, another extremely important use is not for the fruit alone, but for the tree – it makes an excellent ornamental street tree and is planted widely in Arizona and southern California.

Bigarrade Couronnée.

SWEET ORANGE (*Citrus sinensis*)

ABOVE: This single species, *Citrus sinensis* is so widely grown commercially that there are innumerable varieties and cultivars. Some of them make their mark and form a group of their own, such as the navel oranges, common oranges and blood oranges. In fact, so much crossing has gone on over the centuries that a *Citrus* subspecies would seem justified.

CROWNED ORANGE (*Citrus sinensis*)

OPPOSITE: This could be a weird version of the navel orange, which has a secondary orange embedded in the blossom end of its fruit. In this case, and judging by the size of the 'crown', the secondary orange is almost being 'born', for want of a better word.

COMMON CHINA ORANGE (*CITRUS SINENSIS*)

RIGHT: The common or 'sweet' orange is almost hardy and is grown all over the warmer temperate zones and those with a Mediterranean climate. As might be guessed, it is extremely variable in shape and size. So much hybridizing has gone on over the years (both intentionally and naturally) that it barely deserves the title of species.

HORNED ORANGE (*CITRUS AURANTIUM*)

ABOVE: The horned orange and buddha's hand/fingers have the same separation of the fruit into its different segments. This strange fruit is a possible example of a digitated fruit, whose most common cause is *Aceria sheldoni*, a worm-like mite which disrupts fruit development by damaging the buds and flowers of lemon trees, though not often those of other species.

THE BIZARRE ORANGE (*CITRUS AURANTIUM*)

ABOVE: The bizarre *Citrus* was recorded in 1674 by an Italian physician by the name of Pietro Nati, who found it (in around 1645) on a Citron grafted onto a orange tree that was growing in the gardens of a Florentine family's villa. This sort of naturally occurring bud mutation is remarkably wide-ranging in its diversity, and has been recorded within the genus *Citrus* since the seventeenth century.

BERGAMOT (*CITRUS BERGAMIA*)

OPPOSITE: The bergamot orange is was of the most prominent subspecies of the sour orange and has been grown commercially in Italy since the sixteenth century. It is grown predominantly for its aromatic peel, which is used for making scented oils and for flavouring. Trees grown in the USA under the same name are in fact of the ornamental 'Bouquet' variety and not the same plant.

'MALTA BLOOD ORANGE' (*CITRUS SINENSIS*)

ABOVE: The Malta blood orange is one of the best-known and most popular dessert oranges. It is generally accepted that blood oranges, with their red flesh, are the most juicy and have the best flavour. They form about a third of the oranges eaten in the Mediterranean region. In the United, 'Moro', 'Sanguinelli' and 'Tarocco' are preferred varieties.

MANDARIN (*Citrus reticulata*)

BELOW: The organization of the mandarin orange group is
similarly confusing to that of the sweet orange, in that mandarin
covers a multitude of sins. In the UK, the best-known varieties,
or groups, are tangerines, satsumas, true mandarins and
clementines, all of which are small, juicy and easily peeled.

KUMQUAT (*Fortunella margarita*)

RIGHT: Kumquats are orange, egg-shaped fruits about the size
of a small plum. The skin is thick, tender and sweet, and the
flesh is moderately acid. You can eat the entire fruit, skin and
all. In the USA, they are grown in Florida and California, and are
particularly popular at Christmas. Any citrus fruit with 'quat' in
its name has kumquat in its blood.

WATERMELON (*CITRULLUS LANATUS*)

ABOVE AND RIGHT: Although there are round varieties, the typical watermelon is usuallybigger and longer than the rest, although the smaller varieties tend to be the best. All watermelons need dry and hot growing conditions, but with plenty of irrigation water at the roots. In India, they used to be grown on riverbanks, where it is hot, but the roots are able to remain moist. Given the right conditions, these dark-green varieties streaked with white can grow to as much as 1m (3-4ft) long and from 40cm to 50cm (15−20in) in diameter. The bright-red flesh is juicy, cool and refreshing, but sadly its taste is rather insipid.

PETIT CANTALOUP (*CUCUMIS MELO*)

BELOW: The full name of this delicious melon is 'Petit Canteloup des Indes Orientales'. Although it is more of a description than a name, meaning 'Small Cantaloupe from the East Indies'. The Cantaloupes are a far superior group of melons, whose juicy and aromatic orange flesh make the perfect dessert finish to a meal.

'DAMSHA' (*CUCUMIS MELO*)

RIGHT: Sweet melons fall into two broad groups. This one is a honeydew type, with pale-green to whitish flesh that is juicy, sweet and with a mild flavour. They are usually best eaten as the first course of a meal rather than as the dessert, when something a bit 'meatier' is more appropriate.

MELON VARIETIES (*CUCUMIS MELO*)

OPPOSITE: This mouth-watering display shows old cantaloupe-type melons. Many of today's varieties are in this group. They are far tastier than the honeydew type and can be grown just the same as greenhouse cucumbers. Most are a good deal smaller than these older varieties, but are also much easier to grow. Never serve them chilled, as this kills the flavour.

'ROMANA' (*CUCUMIS MELO*)

ABOVE: Looking remarkably like today's 'Dutch Net' melon, this is the sort of cantaloupe variety that was grown in the eighteenth century. The sure way of telling which group a melon belongs to is by looking at the colour of the flesh. Green and white flesh tells us it is a honeydew melon, whereas orange is for a cantaloupe.

'BLACK ROCK' (*CUCUMIS MELO*)

ABOVE: 'Black Rock Cantaloupe' is listed by Abercrombie in *The Complete Kitchen Gardener and Hotbed Forcer* (1789), and was one of the best melons of its day, and also a large one. However, its more obvious claim to fame are the extraordinary warts and outgrowths on its surface. If the flesh was not of such high quality, it would surely be regarded as little more than a curio.

'WHITE SOUTH ROCK' (*CUCUMIS MELO*)

OPPOSITE: With the arrival of improved varieties from France, melons became much more widespread by the mid-seventeenth century. Abercrombie (1789) lists no fewer than thirteen varieties, six of which are cantaloupe. This one is not listed specifically, but 'Rock Cantaleupe' is included and the two varieties must surely be quite similar.

'BLACK JAMAICA'
(*ANANAS COMOSUS*)

LEFT: Pineapples are natives of South
America, and the Earl of Portland
introduced them to England from Holland
in 1690. Brookshaw, the painter of this
portrait, tells us that when it was first
grown in England it aroused such interest
and curiosity that crowned heads and the
aristocracy from France, Holland and
Germany travelled to see it.

'ENVILLE' (*ANANAS COMOSUS*)

OPPOSITE: 'Enville', like 'Black Jamaica'
and 'Queen', is also an old variety.
However, it certainly looked better than it
tasted, for it was described by Hogg as
being a 'very handsome pine, but neither
very rich nor highly flavoured'. This would
certainly account for the shortage of
information on it.

'QUEEN' (*ANANAS COMOSUS*)

ABOVE: The 'Queen' has always been one of the best varieties for growing in England. Even at the start of the twentieth century it headed the list, which also included 'Black Jamaica'. There were three recognized forms of 'Queen' – 'Moscow', 'Ripley' and 'Thorsby'. 'Ripley' was the tenderest of the three, but 'Moscow' had a smaller plant, as well as fruits that were wider than the others.

PINEAPPLE (*ANANAS COMOSUS*)

OPPOSITE: Although the variety of this pineapple is not given, the fact that it was painted by Bonelli suggests that they were already cultivated in Italy around the eighteenth century. Hogg described twenty-five distinct varieties in the late nineteenth century.

PINEAPPLE VARIETIES
(*Ananas comosus*)

RIGHT AND OPPOSITE: Judging by the size of
the fruit and the rough, uneven scales, these are
very low-quality pineapples. However, there is
a good reason for this – it is a picture of what the
pineapple looked like before it was 'tamed' and
brought into cultivation. It could be that the
illustrations show what cultivated pineapples used
to look like after the quality had improved, but
not the fruit size; or maybe the pictures were
painted too far in advance of maturity, which
is certainly what the size of the pine and its
vegetative top would suggest.

PINEAPPLE WITH FLOWER (*ANANAS COMOSUS*)

OPPOSITE: This painting is one of the very few that show both the pineapple flower and fruit. The botanical name, *Bromelia ananas*, is also old. Note that the flower head is a collection of florets. Each develops into a small flower, all of which then grow together to form one compound fruit.

PINEAPPLE WITH BILBERRIES (*ANANAS COMOSUS*)

ABOVE: Whereas the pictures of the two immature or primitive pineapples on the previous spread were essentially lifelike, this one is simply too good to be true. The exaggerated size and smoothness of the fruit, together with the diminutive vegetative top, have taken far too much advantage of artistic licence. The comparative size of the individual bilberries is also rather optimistic.

'DAMSON' (*VITIS VINIFERA*)

ABOVE: Although it is difficult to find more than a passing reference to this grape variety, it seems probable that this is the same as 'Damascus' (bearing in mind that the name 'damson' was a corruption of the word 'Damascus'). This grape is described as having 'large and loose' bunches, and was a first-rate, late glasshouse variety.

'TEINTURIER' (*VITIS VINIFERA*)

OPPOSITE: Like so many of the older fruit varieties (in fact, any other plant), often we are faced with a sole example – the painting. If the fruit was a good variety, it would probably be written about elsewhere, but in many cases we are not so lucky and we are left merely to imagine the story that lies behind the picture.

'TRIFERA' (*VITIS VINIFERA*)

OPPOSITE: References to 'Trifera' are hard to come by. Most books only cover varieties that achieve certain standards of excellence, and any that produces meagre crops like this are hardly likely to commend themselves to gardeners. The secondary bunches have also been allowed to remain, which simply worsens the situation.

'BLACK HAMBURGH' (*VITIS VINIFERA*)

ABOVE: 'Black Hamburgh' is probably the most widely known and best-quality, black dessert variety available for growing in temperate countries. It is unsurpassed outdoors and even under cover it is hard to beat. It is a very old variety, being introduced to England early in the eighteenth century. The most famous example is the vine at Hampton Court Palace, which was planted in 1768.

'LE CAUNELE ROUGE' AND 'LE GRIS COMMUN' (*VITIS VINIFERA*)

ABOVE & RIGHT: With the enormous number of grape varieties that have been bred over thousands of years in cultivation, it is not hard to understand that there must be many which have simply disappeared. This doesn't mean that they aren't worth growing any more, for this is the story of evolution. Where a variety has been superseded, it is because the newer one is better in appearance, crop weight or reliability. Nowadays, the improvements are more sophisticated, covering features such as time of ripening, length of cropping period, and pest and disease resistance.

'MUSCAT ROUGE' (*VITIS VINIFERA*)

ABOVE: Muscat varieties are some of the most famous grapes. Their characteristic flavour – both in the dessert fruits and the wine – are instantly recognizable. Interestingly, this one's anglicised name is not 'Red Muscat' but 'Red Frontignon'. The flesh is juicy, quite firm and has a good musky flavour.

'MUSCAT BLANC' (*VITIS VINIFERA*)

ABOVE: The same naming peculiarity exists here, with its up-to-date title translating as 'White Frontignon'. The bunches are good-looking, but they have no shoulders. The flesh is quite firm and juicy, and possesses a lovely muscat taste.

'CANNON HALL MUSCAT' (*VITIS VINIFERA*)

BELOW: This is a very handsome greenhouse grape (good for showing), which is also of excellent quality. Though not quite up to 'Muscat of Alexandria' for general purposes, there can be no complaints about the fruit's quality, nor its strong muscat flavour.

'MUSCAT OF ALEXANDRIA' (*VITIS VINIFERA*)

OPPOSITE: This is the white greenhouse grape by which the standards of all others are judged, though the portrait doesn't really do credit to the shape of the bunches. These are large, even, strongly triangular and with good shoulders. The fruit is of top quality, but not easy to achieve, since extra heat is needed to bring it to perfection. It has had many seedlings over the years but no other grape has managed to displace its kingly status.

BANANA VARIETIES (*MUSA* X *PARADISIACA*)

ABOVE AND LEFT: The small fruit size suggests that this is
M. chinensis (the Chinese banana) before it changed to *M. cavendishii*
(which, though a familiar name, is no longer considered valid).
M. acuminata is the variety from which all our most familiar bananas are
derived, and is one of the most widely grown dessert bananas because it
is so resistant to wind and disease. The picture left shows the flower
and embryonic fruitlets (fingers). The very bottom of the flower – the
purple bit below the fruitlets – can be used as a vegetable. As they
approach maturity, the bunches of bananas (hands) turn round
completely and point upwards. Surinam is still one of the major
banana-producing countries.

BANANA (*MUSA* x *PARADISIACA*)

ABOVE AND OPPOSITE: The genus *Musa* and its species are one of
those subjects over which the botanists are constantly arguing. What we
do know is that there are two main types of *Musa*. Those that can be
eaten raw as dessert are considered 'true' bananas such as 'Cavendish',
'Gros Michel' and 'apple bananas'. The others, 'plantains', are those
which need to be treated or processed in some way to make them
palatable and digestible. This distinction is man-made and subjective –
all cultivars are merely judged according to their use, be it for eating,
cooking or manufacture.

Musa paradisiaca.   *Bananier Cultivé.*

MANGO (*MANGIFERA INDICA*)

ABOVE: The mango is really the apple of the Tropics in that it is produced throughout that part of the world. There are thousands of varieties, varying in size from plum-like to great big ones the size of melons. Those which are exported to temperate countries are usually of medium size. Being tropical, they are available all year round.

MANGO AND QUINCE (*MANGIFERA INDICA* AND *CYDONIA SINENSIS*)

RIGHT: Strange bed-fellows, but both are 'fruits of the forest', even if the mango is tropical and the quince is from China. The quince makes a very handsome tree – 6–12m (20–40ft) tall and with attractive, peeling bark – but really needs Mediterranean warmth to flower and fruit effectively.

'RED POWIS' AND 'YELLOW POWIS' (*MANGIFERA INDICA*)

OPPOSITE: Although not grown commercially today, unless under different names, these two mango varieties were clearly on the list of desirables in the past, as they have the appearance of a modern mango. Tropical trees are sometimes grown in temperate countries but the mango would not be a wise choice because of its size.

MANGO (*MANGIFERA INDICA*)

ABOVE: Apart from the height of the tree, which can be 30m (100ft) in the wild be or more, the other factors that make mango cultivation away from the Tropics unsuccessful, are the light intensity and day length. The temperature is no problem under glass. Commercially, mango trees are grown on dwarfing rootstocks to make them considerably shorter than they are in the wild.

FEIJOA (*FEIJOA SELLOWIANA*)

OPPOSITE: Named by the German botanist Ernst Berger after a Spanish botanist (Don da Silva Feijoa) and a German specimen collector (F. Sellow), Feijoa is variously termed the 'Pineapple guava' and 'Fig guava', as it tastes something like a pineapple/guava cross. Today, it is mainly cultivated for its value as an ornamental shrub rather than as a dessert fruit.

BREADFRUIT (*ARTOCARPUS ALTILIS*)

ABOVE: The breadfruit's main claim to fame is that it was one of the causes of the 'Mutiny on the Bounty'. The plants that were using the crew's drinking water were on their way from the Pacific to the West Indies when they were thrown over the side along with Captain Bligh (though he had the comparative luxury of a rowing boat).

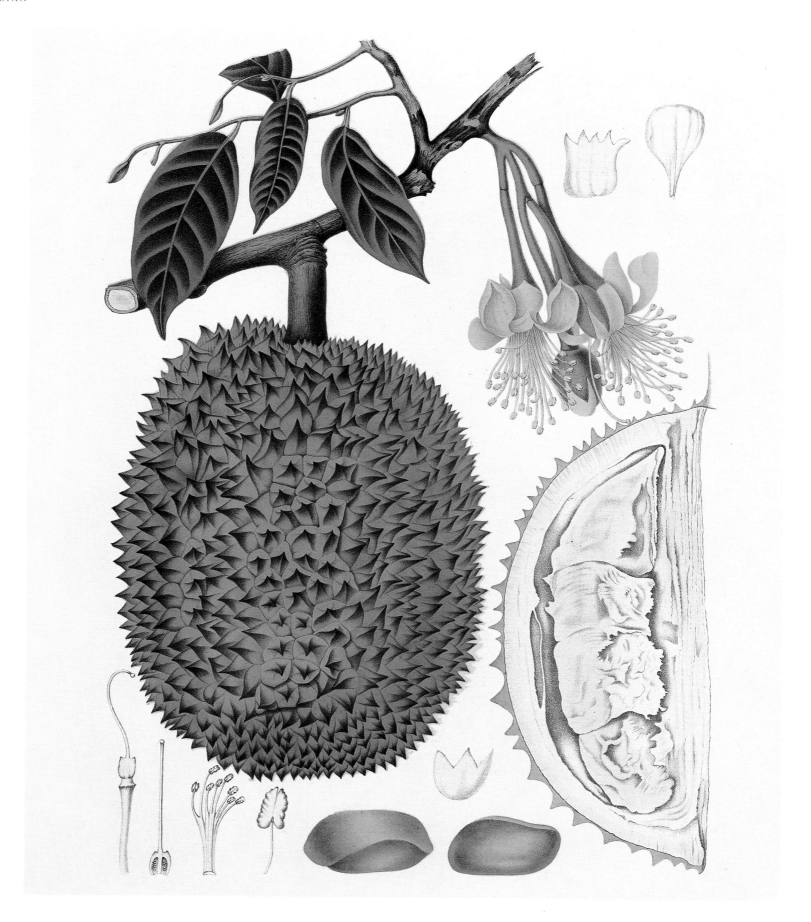

DURIAN (*DURIO ZIBETHINUS*)

ABOVE: The closer the durian gets to maturity, the stronger and more penetrating the smell becomes. It is also covered in spikes. Although its malodorous reputation has won it few defendants in the West, it is still an extremely popular and important native fruit in Southeast Asia – where it is used as a flavouring for ice cream and toothpaste.

CUSTARD APPLE (*ANNONA RETICULATA*)

ABOVE: Also known as the 'Bullock Heart', the custard apple looks rather like a huge fir cone. They are delicious to eat but, sadly, are unlikely to be better known away from their place of origin because of the difficulty of transporting them. They don't travel well and won't tolerate temperatures lower than about 14°C (55°F), so refrigeration is not an option.

STARFRUIT (*AVERRHOA CARAMBOLA*)

OPPOSITE: The starfruit has risen to prominence quite recently with the huge rise in interest in decorative fruit. Sliced crossways, they are very appealing in fruit salads, etc. They come mainly from India and Sri Lanka in two distinct varieties: the so-called 'sweet' variety (containing less than 4 percent sugar), and the 'very sour' variety. Both are still mainly cultivated for looks rather than taste.

TAMARIND (*TAMARINDUS INDICA*)

ABOVE: Coming from India originally but also grown in Indonesia and Africa, the tamarind is a leguminous plant related to carob and manna. All three are pulses and come somewhere between fruits and vegetables. A syrup can be made from tamarin pods and seeds – this keeps well and for a long time in a refrigerator and makes a refreshing drink.

KIWANO
(*CUCUMIS METULIFERUS*)

LEFT: Currently more of a decorative fruit than a dessert variety – due to its bland flavour and acidity – it is perhaps not surprising that the kiwano is little known outside its native home of southern Africa. It was introduced into Australia in the 1930s, where it currently thrives as a weed.

PITAYA (*HYLOCEREUS UNDATUS*)

OPPOSITE: The generic name (*Hylocereus*) indicates that this is a 'woody cactus', and so it turns out to be. Similar to an *Epiphyllum*, it has woody, climbing, triangular stems and large, white flowers. These are followed by large and fleshy seed pods and it is these which are eaten in its native West Indies.

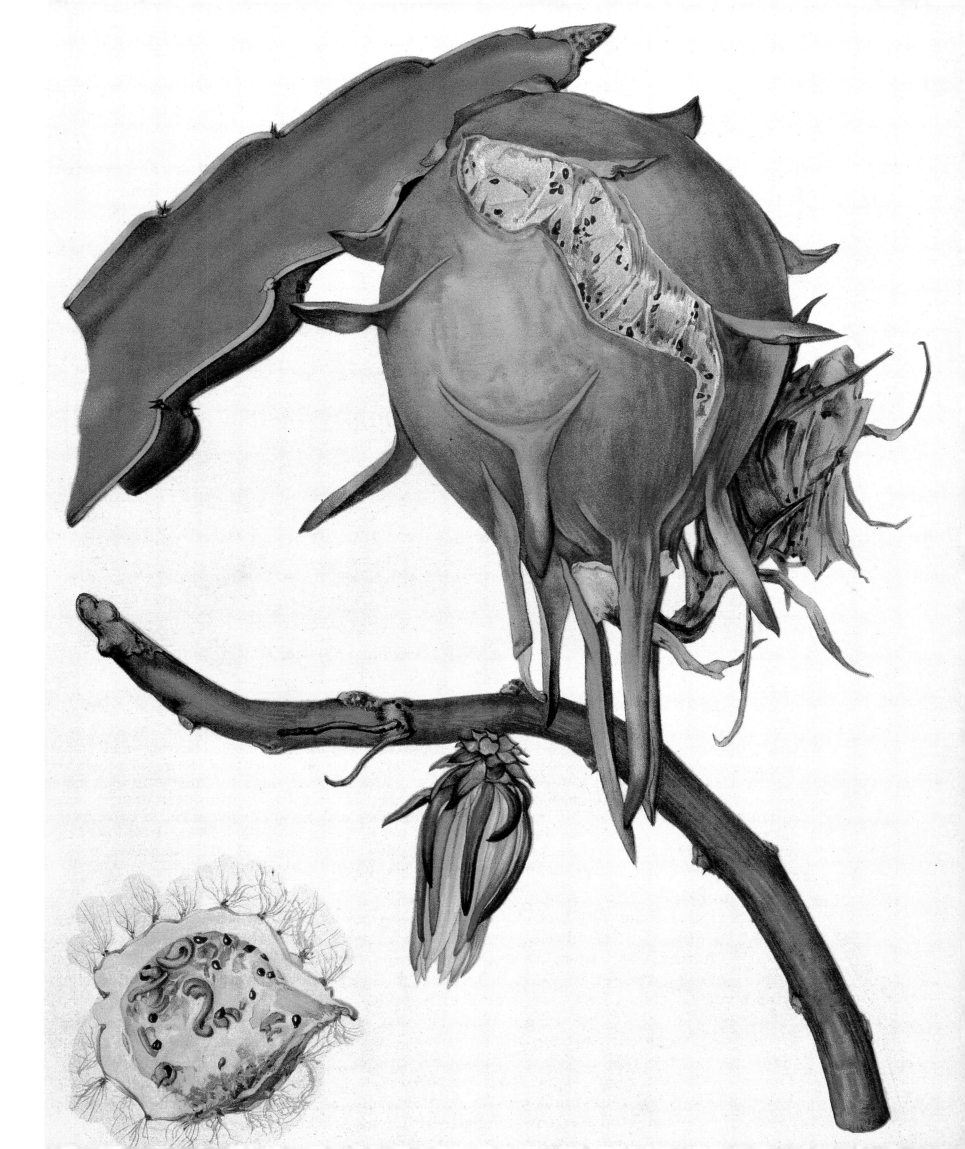

PERSIMMON (*DIOSPYROS KAKI* OR *DIOSPYROS VIRGINIANA*)

ABOVE AND RIGHT: The persimmon is also known as the 'kaki' and, most recently, the 'Sharon Fruit'. It was originally from China and Japan but, with its Mediterranean requirements, it soon spread to anywhere else having a similar climate. This included the southern United States, Brazil, southern France, Spain and Italy. The best in cultivation is the Israeli 'Sharon Fruit'. Unlike the clones grown in most other countries, whose unripe fruits are bitter to the taste, those from Israel are not. The inside of the fruits are divided into compartments filled with soft flesh and pips, and have something of a banana/vanilla taste.

PAPAYA (*CARICA PAPAYA*)

OPPOSITE: The papaya is also called, possibly more commonly, the 'pawpaw'. It is a native of the Tropics, where the soft-stemmed plants (which sremore or less branchless 'trees'), produce clusters of fruits under a tuft of leaves. The fruits taste and appear a look like cantaloupes – prompting early European travellers to nickname them – erroneously – 'tree-melons'.

SAPODILLA (*ACHRAS SAPOTE*)

ABOVE: The widespread cultivation of the sapodilla throughout the Tropics has led to awful confusion over the local names, quality and appearance of the fruits. Believed to originate from Mexico, the flesh of the sapodilla has the texture of an apple but the taste is a mixture of honey, apricot and pears. The sap from the tree (chicle) forms a type of latex and is widely used in the production of chewing gum.

GUAVA (*PSIDIUM GUAJAVA*)

LEFT AND OPPOSITE: Native of tropical America, guavas are now also grown commercially in South Africa, Thailand, Mexico and elsewhere. When ripe, they become soft and give off a lovely scent. Depending on the variety, the flesh can be greenish-white, pink or even dark red. You can eat them on their own or chop them up for fruit salads. Guava flesh has a very distinctive flavour not really like anything else. It's sort of sweet and sharp. They are canned or sold as guava jelly but also used for flavouring ice cream and yoghurt. Like virtually all tropical plants, they are most unlikely to fruit satisfactorily elsewhere.

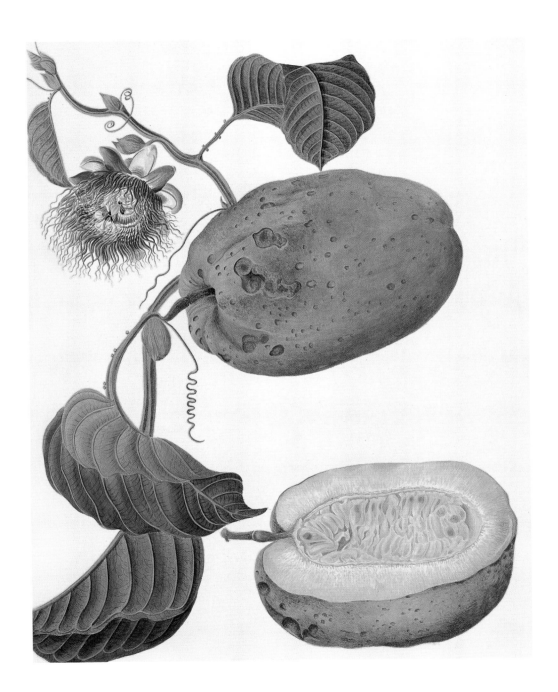

PASSIONFRUIT (*PASSIFLORA EDULIS*)

ABOVE AND OPPOSITE : Out of an estimated five hundred *Passiflora* species, only *Passiflora edulis* is considered a passionfruit without qualification. This variety comes in two distinct types; the purple passionfruit (opposite), which is the preferred dessert variety, and the yellow passionfruit (above) is mainly processed for its juice.

POMEGRANATE (*PUNICA GRANATUM*)

ABOVE AND RIGHT: One way of preparing the fruit for eating is to slit the skin several times from top to bottom, as you would an orange. Hold the fruit over a plate, calyx end down, and pull away the strips of skin. The fleshy pips can then be teased away with a fork. The main commercial pomegranate-growing countries have a subtropical climate, even though the fruit is of Persian origin. Their thick, leathery skins – which turn almost brown if the fruits are kept for a long time – enable pomegranates to be kept juicy over long periods. This has proved a boon to travellers of old, as well as to present-day growers and exporters.

POMEGRANATE
(*PUNICA GRANATUM*)

OPPOSITE AND RIGHT: The
pomegranate has a long, involved and often
fascinating history. One ancient belief was
that every fruit has 613 pips, to correspond
with the number of laws laid down in the
Bible, a 'fact' which is of course difficult to
prove or disprove. The skin and flesh of
the pomegranate exude a juice whose stain
is virtually impossible to remove, and over
the centuries this property has given rise
to the use of the pomegranate in fabric dye
(including the famous Persian rugs and
carpets). Several other species of *Punica* are
grown as ornamental shrubs.

DATE (*PHOENIX DACTYLIFERA*)
LEFT AND OPPOSITE: Cultivation of the
date palm can be traced back to at least
3000 BC in the Middle East. It is now
grown in many countries throughout the
world, including California and Arizona in
the United States. When dried, dates will
keep for a very long time – even from one
Christmas to the next (a mixed blessing,
perhaps!). Date-palm trees are either male
or female, and at least one of each sex is
needed for cultivation. The fruits develop
in the leaf axils high up the tree. Up to
forty clusters can be produced by a tree,
each cluster containing twenty-five to
thirty dates, which adds up to an
impressive total crop per tree of 150kg
(330lb) or so.

MANGOSTEEN (*GARCINIA MANGOSTANA*)

OPPOSITE AND ABOVE: The mangosteen is a strange little fruit about the size of a small tomato. It grows in trees that can reach 25m (80ft) in height, which makes picking rather difficult. A seedling tree can take ten to fifteen years to come into bearing – this is halved when the trees are grown grafted onto seedling rootstocks. The main producers of mangosteens are the Far East, Central America and Brazil. Beneath its thick skin, the syrupy flesh is divided into sections. The flesh is waxy-white and has the refreshing taste of a mixture of grapes and peaches. All this makes the mangosteen an expensive fruit to grow.

LANGSTAT (*LANSIUM DOMESTICUM*)

OPPOSITE: The langstat comes from the tropical Far East, where the trees are about the same size as those of the mangosteen. Practically every village, and certainly every district, has a different name for the fruit. The langstat's appearance also varies from tree to tree. Its juice is milky and bitter, and its flesh sour and translucent, so it doesn't have much going for it really.

LOQUAT (*ERIOBOTRYA JAPONICA*)

ABOVE: The loquat, or Japanese medlar, is small, pear-shaped and yellow, and tastes like a mixture of apple and apricot. It comes from China and Japan, but it is now grown by many other subtropical countries. The tree has large, sweet chestnut-shaped leaves and is almost hardy, though it needs more warmth to fruit. Its large pips germinate quite easily.

RAMBUTAN (*NEPHELIUM LAPPACEUM*)

OPPOSITE: From the outside, the rambutan looks like a lychee with whiskers. The flesh, which lies between the skin and the seed, is pale yellow, juicy and pleasant, but is not really up to that of the lychee. It comes from Malaysia and Indonesia (where it is grown commercially), as well as in Thailand. They make a good dessert fruit, and you can also find them in a canned variety.

LONGAN (*DIMOCARPUS LONGAN*)

ABOVE: The longan is also known as the 'Dragon's Eye' and (botanically) as *Euphoria longana*. The family *Sapindaceae* has a number of these fairly similar fruits within its doors: as well as the lungen, there is the lychee and rambutan. They are the size of small plums and have a characteristic firmish skin, translucent jelly-like flesh and a single large seed.

LYCHEE (*LITCHI CHINENSIS*)

ABOVE AND RIGHT: The fruits of the lychee are borne in large clusters. Each
fruit is about the size of a plum, and has an easily removable, rough, thin rind. In
southern India and Mauritius, there are two crops a year, in May and December.
Several lychee varieties are cultivated, their main distinctions being size, shape and
fruit quality. The lychee is undoubtedly the most well-known of the *Sapindaceae*
family, and almost certainly the best. Although of Chinese origin, they are now also
grown in Israel, South Africa and Thailand. Lychees are available both fresh and in
cans, and are much loved by Chinese restaurants in Britain. Interestingly, the fruit's
large stone/seed/pip can also be roasted and eaten.

CHINESE LANTERN
(*PHYSALIS ALKEKENGI*)

OPPOSITE: Another name for this is the bladder cherry. It is not the same as either the cape gooseberry (*P. peruviana*), which is a higher-quality fruit, or the chinese lantern of gardens (the hardier *P. franchetii*). However, it does produce a red, edible berry within the lantern part, and the plant is hardier than the cape gooseberry.

CAPE GOOSEBERRY
(*PHYSALIS PERUVIANA*)

RIGHT: Despite its name, the cape gooseberry comes from Mexico rather than Peru. Reputedly cultivated by settlers at the Cape of Good Hope, it was then transported to Australia, where it assumed its English common name. Predominantly used for preserves and sauces – the cape gooseberry can today be found the world over.

Olive Picholine!

'PICHOLINE' AND 'GALLETTE' (*OLEA EUROPAEA*)

ABOVE AND OPPOSITE: The original homes of the European olive are Asia Minor and Greece. However, over more than a thousand years it has become indigenous thoughout the Mediterranean area. The olive is one of the only things that can be grown on the hills and mountains of the Mediterranean region, where the soil is desperately poor. While those olives grown for oil are left to mature on the trees, those for pickling and stuffing. are gathered slightly immature. Prior to bottling, these are soaked, in order to remove some of the fruit's bitterness. The wood of old or dead olive trees is highly prized for the intricate patterns that are formed in the grain.

OLEA SATIVA Amygdaeformis
Ulive Gallette

AVOCADO PEAR (*PERSEA GRATISSIMA*)

OPPOSITE AND ABOVE: The avocado pear originally came from Central and South America, but its commercial production has spread to Israel, southern Africa, the United States, Central and South America and Spain, which means it is available all year round. Also, the fruits travel very well because they are picked when quite hard and unripe, ripening perfectly at room temperature. The avocado is a remarkable fruit because it is only about seventy per cent water (rather than the ninety-five to ninety-eight per cent of most other fruit). The rest is mainly unsaturated fatty acids, so very low in cholesterol and therefore easily digested. When it is fully ripe, the stone normally comes free, rattling when the fruit is shaken. Fully ripe avocados taste the best of all.

COCONUT
(*COCUS NUCIFERA*)

RIGHT AND OPPOSITE: What we view
to be a coconut is actually just the seed of
the palm tree – the fibre on the outside is
the seed-coat. Of the three sealed holes at
one end, two are just indentations, whereas
the third is a plugged hole through which
the germinating seed grows. Coconuts
come from all over Asia, not just from sun-
drenched beaches on desert islands. The
major industrial use of coconuts is to
produce an oil from which soap and
margarine are made (hence the familiar
coconut-like taste of some margarines).
The dried flesh can be ground into
desiccated coconut, for use in cooking,
while other uses include coconut shies at
fairs and winter treats for tits and other
small birds.

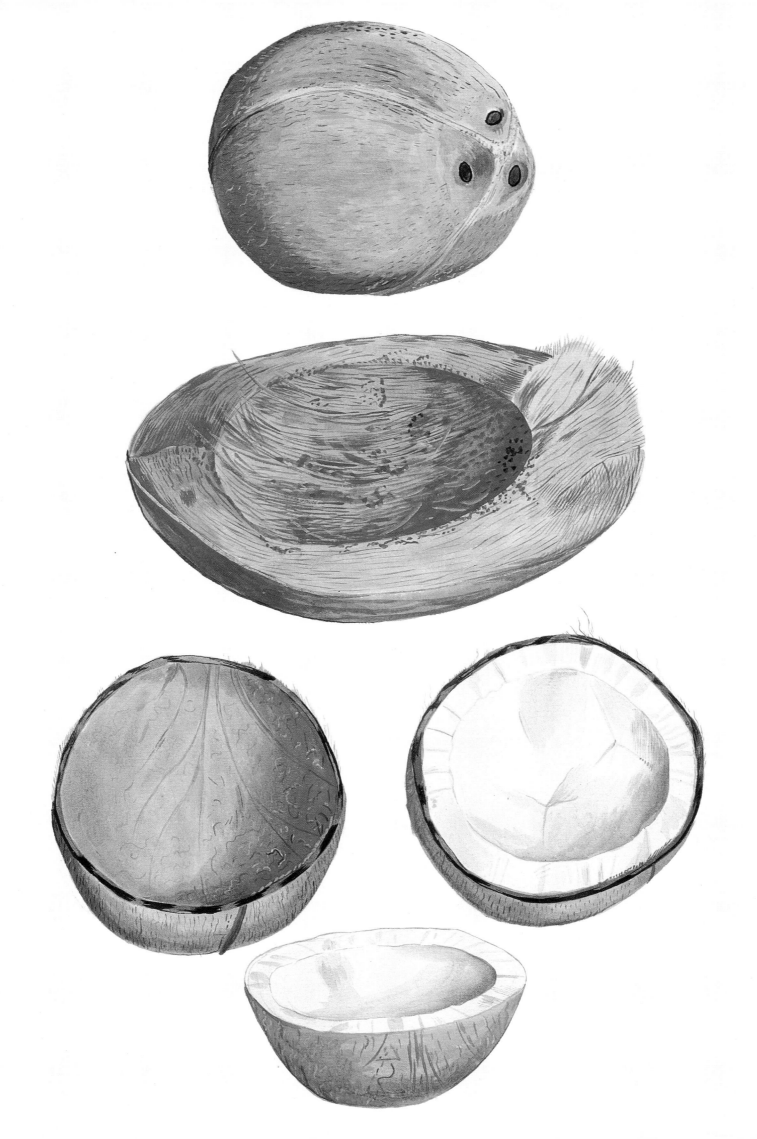

1.   5.

11.   12.   13.   14.   15.   10.

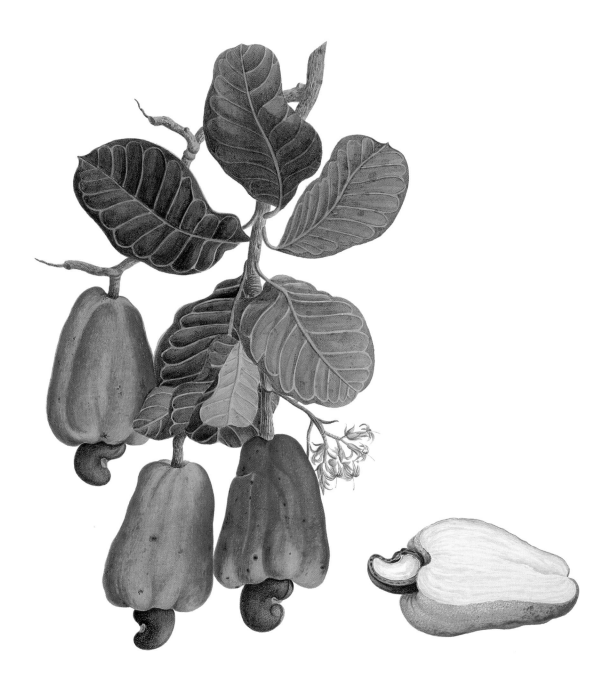

CASHEW NUT (*ANACARDIUM OCCIDENTALE*)

ABOVE: There is a lot more to cashew nuts than meets the eye. The fruit consists of two distinct parts: a large, fleshy, pear-shaped stalk called the cashew apple, to which is attached the kidney-shaped nut with an edible kernel, which is roasted to make it edible. They come from tropical America and the West Indies, but have become naturalized in Africa.

PISTACHIO NUT (*PISTACIA VERA*)

OPPOSITE: This is another slightly odd fruit. What we call the nut comes from a tree, and consists of a thin-shelled capsule that contains the seed. This seed is green and, when roasted and eaten, has a pleasant rather than spectacular taste. The pistachio is also used in sweet- and ice-cream making, to add extra flavouring.

WALNUT (*JUGLANS REGIA*)

ABOVE AND OPPOSITE: The walnut tree is much prized for its high-quality furniture timber, but is also known for its nut production. Walnut trees can take fifteen to twenty years to come into bearing, but new and dwarfer varieties that start to produce nuts in under five years are becoming available. Walnuts that are wanted for the nuts themselves are either shaken or knocked from the tree when the outer husk starts to split, but are best left to fall. Those nuts required for pickling are gathered, green, during July.

ALMOND (*PRUNUS DULCIS*)

OPPOSITE AND ABOVE: Almond trees very seldom produce useful nuts away from the
Mediterranean region, where the growing seasons are longer, the summer temperatures are higher,
and where they are grown in orchards like any other fruit tree. However, only the nut of the almond
is eaten, whereas with all its *Prunus* relatives the fleshy outside is the edible part. In the eighteenth
and nineteenth centuries, argument was rife in England as to the rightful position of the almond
within the *Prunus* genus. Knight considered it to be an inferior form of peach, and Charles Darwin
joined him in believing that careful selections of almond seedlings would eventually result in a
peach tree. Later, Thomas Rivers considered that peaches would eventually degenerate into thick-
fleshed almonds. Even the specific name changes periodically.

Biographies

EDWARD BUNYARD (1878–1939)

took over one of the great English fruit nurseries on the death of his father George (V.M.H.) in 1919. One of Bunyard's early achievements was *The Handbook of Fruits*, which filled the gap left by Hogg's *Fruit Manual*, last printed in 1884. Besides his immense ability as a nurseryman, Bunyard was a great connoisseur of fruit and wine, a *bon viveur* and lover of all things good. This is borne out by his delightful, classic book, *The Anatomy of Dessert – With a Few Notes on Wine* (1929). He had a beautiful way of condemning something with faint praise. Another of Bunyard's works was the *Epicure's Companion*, which he wrote with his sisters, Lorna and Frances. Bunyard had great knowledge of the history of fruit and fruit growing.

DR GEORGE MCMILLAN DARROW (1889–1983)

was, for many years, the USA's foremost authority on small (soft) fruits. His whole professional career (1911–57) was spent with the US Department of Agriculture, and he was appointed administrative head of its Small Fruits Research Section in 1945. He was noted for his extensive knowledge of fruit crops (especially the strawberry and blueberry), and was also a prolific writer, with more than two hundred published works to his name. Probably his greatest was *The Strawberry – History, Breeding and Physiology*, published in 1966. Darrow is best known for his breeding, genetics and disease-resistance studies with strawberries, raspberries and blueberries. The American strawberry cultivar 'Blakemore' was his first triumph in 1929, and set the standard for fruit firmness, quickly becoming the most important cultivar in the USA (a position it held for twenty years). Darrow organized teams to study red stele root-rot (red-core) resistance, virus indexing and certified plant production of the strawberry. After he retired in 1957, he began collecting and breeding day lilies – another crop for which he was well-known.

JOHN GERARD (1545–1612)

was a barber-surgeon by profession and went on to become curator of the London College of Physicians' garden of medicinal plants. The garden quite rightly contained many fruits that fitted in with his wide knowledge of all plants with medicinal properties. He had a garden of his own in Holborn, London, of which he published a catalogue – in fact, the first complete garden catalogue ever published. He was also responsible for Lord Burghley's gardens in the Strand, London and at Theobald's in Hertfordshire. It is for his *Great Herball* (1597) that John Gerard will always be remembered, however. He was commissioned to write it by Elizabeth I's printer, John Norton, as an accompaniment to pictures that Norton had rented from Germany. It is unquestionably the fullest and most famous herbal to be produced in England, and after his death it ran to another two revised editions, these being produced by Thomas Johnston in 1633 and 1639.

RICHARD HARRIS (C.1530)

planted and managed the first large, commercially run orchard/fruit nursery in England. By Henry VIII's reign, many different fruits were becoming popular in England, although the best trees and varieties still came from other parts of Europe. In 1533, Harris (who was the king's fruiterer) rented a piece of land belonging to the king at Osiers Farm, Teynham, in Kent. He started by planting cherries there, which are still grown in the area. The New Garden came next which was on a much bigger scale, containing many imported trees. From Holland, he brought cherries and pears, and from France mainly 'Pippins' and 'Golden Reinette' – until then, there were virtually no dessert apples in England. News of his success in large-scale fruit growing must have spread quickly, because fruit planting shortly started in earnest all over the country. Many people sent to the New Garden for graft- and bud-wood. Harris' trees were the 'mother' trees for most English orchards planted at about that time and greatly

LEFT TO RIGHT:
Edward Bunyard
John Gerard
Sir Ronald George Hatton

increased the number of varieties being grown. Very little is known about Harris himself, except that he was born in Ireland, came to London and almost certainly had a house in Teynham.

SIR RONALD GEORGE HATTON, CBE, MA, DSC, FRS, VMH (1886–1965)

worked at East Malling Research Station (EMRS) in Kent for thirty-five years, thirty of them as its director. He saw it grow from an 8-hectare (20-acre) field and hut to a 146-hectare (360-acre) fruit farm and experimental station with modern laboratories and a scientific staff of eighty. He trained at the South-Eastern Agricultural College in Wye, near Canterbury, where he later worked, and transferred to the newly born Wye College Fruit Experiment Station at East Malling, the fledgling EMRS. There he worked under Wellington, the first director, later becoming acting director, and then director in 1919 (a post he held until he retired in 1949). Hatton's work on classifying and developing modern rootstocks is still recognized as the most important ever carried out. Soon after he became director, the first major steps were taken towards building EMRS into the leading fruit research station in the world. He played a pivotal part in setting up the National Agricultural Advisory Service (NAAS), the National Fruit Trials at Wisley, and also the Fruit Group of the Royal Horticultural Society, of which he was the first chairman. The Hatton Fruit Garden, in the grounds of Bradbourne House (EMRS), commemorates his life and work.

JESSE HIATT (C.1870)

Jesse Hiatt was a Quaker farmer who lived near Peru in Iowa. In the 1870s, he found a chance sucker that had sprung up from an apple rootstock on his farm. He tried twice (and failed) to chop it out, so when it sprouted a third time he let it grow. Once the tree started to fruit, he discovered qualities in it that he liked. In 1893, he displayed it as 'Hawkeye' at a fruit show in Louisiana, Missouri.

The following year, the Stark Brothers Nurseries & Orchards Co bought the propagating rights and renamed the apple 'Delicious'. Many genetic variations have appeared over the years, including 'Red Delicious', which is a cloned and highly coloured sport of the original 'Delicious'. It is a glossy red apple with distinctive five-pointed shoulders and an oblong to oblong-conical shape, and is best eaten fresh, when it has a juicy, crunchy texture and a sweet flavour. Whether or not this discovery merits Jesse Hiatt's inclusion in this book depends on one's opinion of his apple. However, the 'Delicious' is the most popular apple variety in the entire world – including the United States – and that in itself must be worth something.

DR ROBERT HOGG LLD (1818–97)

was editor of the *Journal of Horticulture* in London for many years. During this time, he wrote his masterpiece, *The Fruit Manual* (1860), which ran to five editions, the last one being issued in 1884. He wrote several other books on fruit and its production, and was technical editor for the *Herefordshire Pomona* (1885), which was illustrated by William Hooker (q.v.). Hogg became involved in the work of the Royal Horticultural Society and soon became its fruit 'backbone'. He served as vice president, and as its secretary, and was twice the secretary of the Fruit and Vegetable Committee (the first period ended with his resignation, when he considered that the Society was wasting money; he was persuaded to return to the post later). Hogg was an original member of the Lindley Library Trust and remained highly active in the affairs of the RHS, especially the Fruit and Vegetable Committee, right until his death. Another of his responsibilities was to superintend the selection of plants for replanting the Society's Fruit Garden at Chiswick. Robert Hogg was never awarded the VMH; he died just months before it came into being. However, in 1898, the Hogg Medal for Fruit was introduced to commemorate him.

WILLIAM HOOKER (1779–1832)

should not be confused with Sir William Jackson Hooker, himself a skilled botanical artist and a professor of botany. Sadly, little is known about William Hooker before he became a botanical artist, but his botanical portraits and other paintings of plants and fruits stand supreme. His knowledge of fruit (especially) was remarkable and, early in the nineteenth century, the Horticultural Society of London (later the RHS) commissioned him to paint and describe around 150 of the most interesting and attractive kinds and varieties of fruit then in cultivation. Many of these portraits have become famous all over the world and have been used in many different ways. One of the most popular is a collection of bone-china plates, vases, jugs, teapots, etc. decorated with his fruit portraits. These were produced and sold by the RHS in the 1990s. Hooker's originals are among the most-prized possessions of the RHS. They are now kept in the Lindley Library, and a great many of them are featured in this book.

THOMAS ANDREW KNIGHT (1759–1838)

was a founder member of the Horticultural Society of London (later the RHS) and became its president (1811–38). His book *Treatise on the Culture of the Apple and Pear and on the Manufacture of Cider and Perry* was published in 1797. His theory – that all varieties of fruit have a fixed life, after which they gradually decay and die – was quite widely held in those days. Although he was mistaken in this belief, it inspired him to breed new varieties along wholly scientific lines. To this end, he used only the best available varieties for crossing. He was made a Fellow of the Royal Society in 1804. His most famous book, *Pomona Herefordensis* (not to be confused with *Herefordshire Pomona*), appeared in 1811. He remained an avid plant breeder and, in 1814, released the cherries 'Black Eagle', 'Elton' and 'Waterloo', which are all listed and grown today. He also bred apples, pears, plums, peaches and nectarines, strawberries, redcurrants and grapes. Knight's work with cider

apples and cider laid the foundations for the cider industry. His name is commemorated in the RHS Knightian Medal.

LAXTON BROS OF BEDFORD (EST. 1860)

is known in the fruit world as one of the great fruit nurseries and breeders. Thomas Laxton, also a distinguished geneticist and noted for his work on pea breeding, started the nursery in 1860 and died in 1890, at the age of just 60. His work was continued by his sons, Edward (VMH in 1932) and William, from whom the nursery took its name. Laxton's list of home-bred fruit, vegetable and flower varieties (of which there were 170 by 1930) reads like a role of honour. The apples 'Laxton's Fortune' (now 'Fortune'), 'Laxton's Superb' and 'Lord Lambourne', and the 'Early Laxton' plum are (even nowadays) excellent garden varieties. Probably their best-known and greatest introduction was the strawberry 'Royal Sovereign' – released in 1892, it was a cross between 'Noble' and 'King of the Earlies' (both Laxton varieties), and many people think it is still unsurpassed for flavour. Edward Laxton died in 1951, at the age of 82.

SIR JAMES MOUNT CBE, BEM, VMH (1908–94)

was one of England's biggest and most up-to-date fruit farmers. With his brother David, he took over the family's farming and fruit-growing business on the death of their father. He developed S.W. Mount & Sons into one of the largest farming businesses of its kind, covering four separate farms and totalling 490 hectares (1200 acres). Eventually, he had well over 810 hectares (2000 acres) of fruit. Jim Mount was appointed to the governing body of East Malling Research Station (EMRS) in 1944, became its chief executive in 1945, chairman of the Finance Committee in 1948 and succeeded Sir Thomas Neame as chairman in 1959, a post he held for twenty years. He remained on the governing body until 1981 and on the Trust until he retired in 1993. In 1961 he helped to found (and became the first chairman of) Home Grown Fruits,

LEFT TO RIGHT:
Dr. Robert Hogg
Thomas Andrew Knight
Thomas Laxton
Edward Laxton
Sir James Mount
Sir Thomas Neame
Thomas Rivers

later to merge (on the very day he died) with East Kent Packers to form the English Fruit Company (ENFRU), about which he would have been delighted. He was appointed CBE in 1965 and was knighted in 1979 for his services to British horticulture. In 1992, the new apple storage research facility at EMRS was opened and named the Jim Mount Building.

SIR THOMAS NEAME MBE, VMH (1885–1972)

came from a well-known and well-respected Kent farming family. He started his career in industry but returned home to manage the farms when his father, Frederick Neame, died. His greatest interest was in apple and pear growing and he had a large collection of varieties at home, with which he won many Gold Medals at RHS autumn shows in London. Thomas Neame held many prestigious positions, including an RHS council member and chairman of its Fruit Group, chairman of the governing body of East Malling Research Station (EMRS). He was on the governing council of the John Innes Institute, High Sheriff of Kent, and was on the council of the Royal Agricultural Society. As well as his services to research, Neame was a firm believer in the cooperative marketing of fruit, and it was under his leadership that East Kent Packers became the leading cooperative enterprise in the country. He was knighted in 1960 for his services to horticulture. Thomas Neame always encouraged younger fruit growers and many benefited from his advice. He was a perfectionist, but never asked for more than he was prepared to give.

JEAN-BAPTISTE DE LA QUINTINYE (1624–88)

a lawyer by training and profession, took up horticulture when he was 54 years old. In his first horticultural job, he was in charge of the Orangerie and the old *potager* (kitchen garden) at Versailles. However, he was soon asked to lay out a new *potager* to the south of the Orangerie and palace. Thus began the project for which he will always be remembered – the construction of the of Potager du Roi (King's Kitchen Garden) at Versailles. Describing the site, he said that 'The soil on which I had to create the *potager* was of a kind that no one would like to find anywhere.' To make enough room for all the trained fruit trees that would be needed, he created a central square, surrounded by small gardens isolated by walls and terraces. The whole place, which covered an area of 9 hectares (22 acres), was enclosed by high walls. It took from 1678 to 1683 to complete and he remained in charge of the project until his death. De la Quintinye was a pioneer of forcing early crops: using frames, greenhouses and the small, sheltered plots, he provided the king with a wide range of out-of-season fruits and vegetables – strawberries in April, figs and melons in June. His literary masterpiece, *Instructions pour les jardins fruitiers et potagers (Instructions for Fruit and Vegetable Gardens)*, was published in France in 1690, after his death, and was later translated into English by John Evelyn.

THOMAS RIVERS & SON LTD (EST 1725)

Thomas Rivers (1798–1877) of Sawbridgeworth in Hertfordshire, England, was at first a rose specialist, but he later turned to fruit and carried out important work on root pruning, double grafting, orchard houses, cordon training and breeding new varieties. Peaches and nectarines were his speciality and his 'Hawk' family of peach varieties included two particularly good specimens – 'Sea Eagle' and 'Peregrine' are both grown today. By the time of his death, he had raised and fruited 1500 candidate peach seedlings under glass. In his later years, he was assisted by his son Francis, and on his father's death Francis continued to work on new varieties, concentrating more on apples, pears and cherries. His best-known introductions were the 'Conference' pear and 'Early Rivers' cherry, both of which are extremely important. For all his work, he was awarded the first Hogg Medal in 1898. Francis Rivers, VMH (awarded in 1897), was an RHS council member and died in 1899, at the age of 68.

Illustrations

All images sourced from the Lindley Library of the Royal Horticultural Society.

Please note that some of the images appearing in this book are details from the existing artworks.

from *Pomona Britannica* (1812),
by George Brookshaw.
255 'Enville', *Ananas comosus*,
illustration by William Hooker, (1817).
256 Pineapple, *Ananas comosus*, from
Hortus Romanus (1772), by
Giogio Bonelli.
257 'Queen', *Ananas comosus*,
illustration by William Hooker, (1817).
258/9 Pineapple Varieties, *Ananas
comosus*, from *Regne Vegetale* (1831),
by Pierre Ledoulx.
260 Pineapple with flower (Bromelia),
Ananas comosus, from *Les Liliacées*
(1802), by Pierre Joseph Redoute.
261 Pineapple with Bilberries,
Ananas comosus, illustration by
Lui Chi Wang (c.1800).
262 'Damson', *Vitis vinifera*,
illustration by William Hooker (1817).
263 'Teinturier', *Vitis vinifera*, from
Pomologie Francaise (1838-46),
by Pierre-Antoine Poiteau.
264 'Trifera', *Vitis vinifera*, from
Pomona Italiana (1839), Vol 2, by
Giorgio Gallesio. Illustration by
Isabella Bozzolini.
265 'Black Hamburgh', *Vitis vinifera*,
from *Hooker's drawings of Fruit*, Vol 3,
pl 13, by William Hooker (1818).
266 'Le Caunele Rouge', *Vitis vinifera*,
from *Abbildung aller Oekonomische
Pflanzen* (1786-96), by
Johannes Kerner.
267 'Le Gris Commun', *Vitis vinifera*,
from *Abbildung aller Oekonomische
Pflanzen* (1786-96), by
Johannes Kerner.
268 'Muscat Rouge', *Vitis vinifera*, from
Abbildung aller Oekonomische Pflanzen
(1786-96), by Johannes Kerner.
269 Muscat Blanc, *Vitis vinifera*, from
Pomologie Française (1838-46), Vol 2,
pl 50, by Pierre-Antoine Poiteau.
270 'Cannon Hall Muscat', *Vitis
vinifera*, illustration by Augusta
Withers (1825).
271 'Muscat of Alexandria', *Vitis
vinifera*, from *Pomona Britannica*
(1812), by George Brookshaw.
272 Banana, *Musa* x *paradisiaca*, from
Surinam Orchids (1830), Vol 1, pl 122,
by John Henry Lance.
273 Banana, *Musa* x *paradisiaca*, from
Flore des Antilles (1808), by
F. R. de Tussac.
274/5 Banana, *Musa* x *paradisiaca*,
from *Les Liliacées* (1802), by Pierre
Joseph Redoute.
276 Mango, *Mangifera indica*, from *Horti
Malabarici* (1774), by Hendrick Rheede.

277 Mango and Quince, *Mangifera
indica* & *Cydonia sinensis*, illustration
by Lui Chi Wang (c.1800).
278 'Red Powis' & 'Yellow Powis',
Mangifera indica, illustration by
Augusta Withers (1826).
279 Mango, *Mangifera indica*, from
Surinam Orchids (1830), Vol 1, pl 85,
by John Henry Lance.
280 Feijoa, *Feijoa sellowiana*, from
Revue Horticole (1898).
281 Breadfruit, *Artocarpus altilis*,
from *Flore des Antilles* (1808), by F. R.
de Tussac. Illustration by Pierre
J. F. Turpin.
282 Durian, *Durio Zibethinus*, from
Fleurs, Fruits... de Java (1863), by
Berthe Hoole van Nooten.
283 Custard Apple, *Annona reticulata*,
from *Surinam Orchids* (1830), Vol 1,
pl 88, by John Henry Lance.
284 Starfruit, *Averrhoa Carambola*,
from *Trans. Hort. Soc., London* (1842),
by Sarah Drake.
285 Tamarind, *Tamarindus indica*,
illustration by Claude Aubrier (1720).
286 Kiwano, *Cucumis metuliferus*,
from *Botanical Magazine* (1911).
287 Pitaya, *Hylocereus undatus*, from
The Cactaceae (1919), Vol 2,
pl XXXII, by N. L. Briton & J. N.
Rose. Illustration by M. E. Eaton.
288 Persimmon, (Sharon Fruit),
Diospyros kaki or Diospyros virginiana,
from *Botanical Magazine* (1907).
289 Persimmon, (Sharon Fruit),
Diospyros kaki or Diospyros virginiana,
illustration by John Reeves (1812-31).
290 Papaya, *Carica papaya*, from
Fleurs, Fruits... de Java (1863), by
Berthe Hoole van Nooten.
291 Sapodilla, *Achras sapote*, from
Flore des Antilles (1808), by
F. R. de Tussac.
292 Guava, *Psidium guajava*, from
Flore pittoresque (1829), by Michael
Etienne Descourtilz.
293 Guava, *Psidium guajava*, from
Surinam Orchids (1825), Vol 1, pl 109,
by Gerrit Schouten.
294 Passionfruit, *Passiflora edulis*,
from *Trans. Hort. Soc., London*, (1820).
295 Passionfruit, (Giant Granadilla),
Passiflora edulis, from *Surinam
Orchids* (1823), by Gerrit Schouten.
296 Pomegranate, *Punica granatum*,
from *Pomologie Française* (1838-46),
by Pierre-Antoine Poiteau.
297 Pomegranate, *Punica granatum*,
illustration by Lui Chi Wang (c.1810).
298 Pomegranate, *Punica granatum*,

from *Flore medicale* (1814), by
Francois P. Chaumeton. Illustration
by Pierre J. F. Turpin.
299 Pomegranate, *Punica granatum*,
from *A Curious Herbal*, (1739),
pl 145, by Elizabeth Blackwell.
300 Date, *Phoenix dactylifera*, from
Flore pittoresque (1829), by Michel
Etienne Descourtilz.
301 Date, *Phoenix dactylifera*, from
Traite des Arbres Fruitiers (first
published in 1768) by Henri Louis
Duhamel du Monceau.
302 Mangosteen, *Garcinia mangostana*,
from *Fleurs, Fruits...de Java* (1863), by
Berthe Hoole van Nooten.
303 Mangosteen, *Garcinia mangostana*, from *Tropical Fruits Book*
(c.1840), pl 17.
304 Langstat, *Lansium domesticum*,
from *Fleurs, Fruits...de Java* (1863),
by Berthe Hoole van Nooten.
305 Loquat, *Eriobotrya japonica*, from
Trans. Hort. Soc., London, (1822).
306 Rambutan, *Nephelium lappaceum*,
from *Fleurs, Fruits...de Java* (1863), by
Berthe Hoole van Nooten.
307 Longan, *Dimocarpus longan*, from
Trans. Hort. Soc., London (1817),
Vol 2, pl XXVIII.
308 Lychee, *Litchi chinensis*,
illustration by Lui Chi Wang, (c.1800).
309 Lychee, *Litchi chinensis*,
illustration by John Reeves (c.1800).
310 Chinese Lantern, *Physalis
alkekengi*, from *Abbildung aller
Oekonomische Pflanzen* (1786-96),
by Johannes Kerner.
311 Cape Gooseberry, *Physalis
peruviana*, from *Flore Pittoresque*
(1829), pl 248, by Michel
Etienne Descourtilz.
312 'Picholine' (Olive), *Olea europaea*,
from *Pomologie Française* (1838-46),
by Pierre-Antoine Poiteau.
313 'Gallette' (Olive), *Olea europaea*,
illustration by Muzzi for Antonio
Targioni-Tozzetti.
314 Avocado Pear, *Persea gratissima*,
from *Surinam Orchids* (1830), Vol 1,
pl 113, by John Henry Lance.
315 Avocado Pear, *Persea gratissima*,
from *Tropical Fruits Book* (c. 1840),
pl 23. Anon.
316 Coconut, *Cocus nucifera*, from
Tropics (c.1825). Anon.
317 Coconut, *Cocus nucifera*, from
Tropics (c.1825). Anon.
318 Pistachio Nut, *Pistacia vera*, from
Pomologie Française, (1838-46), Vol 1,
pl 8, by Pierre-Antoine Poiteau.

319 Cashew Nut, *Anacardium
occidentale*, from *Tropical Fruits Book*
(c.1840), pl 26. Anon.
320 Walnut, (Large French),
Juglans regia, illustration by William
Hooker (1816).
321 Walnut ('High flyer'), *Juglans
regia*, illustration by William
Hooker (1820).
322 Almond, *Prunus dulcis*, from
Pomologie Française (1838-46), Vol 1,
pl 12, by Pierre- Antoine Poiteau.
Illustration by Pierre J. F. Turpin.
323 Almond, *Prunus dulcis*, from
Pomologie Française (1838-46), Vol 1,
pl 5, by Pierre-Antoine Poiteau.

BIOGRAPHIES

325 (left) Mr. Edward A. Bunyard,
held by The Lindley Library at The
Royal Horticultural Society.
325 (centre) John Gerard, held by
The Lindley Library at The Royal
Horticultural Society.
325 (right) Sir Ronald George Hatton,
photograph by Walter Stoneman, of
J. Russell & Sons, Baker St., London.
Held by The Lindley Library at
The Royal Horticultural Society.
326 (left) Dr. Robert Hogg, held by
The Lindley Library at The Royal
Horticultural Society.
326 (centre left) Thomas Andrew
Knight, held by The Lindley Library
at The Royal Horticultural Society.
326 (centre right) Thomas Laxton,
held by The Lindley Library at
The Royal Horticultural Society.
326 (right) Edward Laxton, held by
The Lindley Library at The Royal
Horticultural Society.
327 (left) Sir James Mount,
photograph by the Kentish Gazette,
9 St. Georges Place, Canterbury. Held
by The Lindley Library at The Royal
Horticultural Society.
327 (centre) Sir Thomas Neame,
photograph by Navana Vandyk,
29 New Bond St., London. Held by
The Lindley Library at The Royal
Horticultural Society.
327 (right) Thomas Rivers, held by
The Lindley Library at The Royal
Horticultural Society.

ACKNOWLEDGEMENTS

336 Early illustration from *Fruit Trees*
(1696), by Thomas Langford.

index

Acknowledgements

The following, and many others too numerous to mention, are due my especial thanks for the invaluable help that they have given me in both the writing of this book and during what is already my long and happy working life. All of them are old friends of mine; some very old! and there are others, sadly, now beyond our reach. My life would be all the poorer without them.

Jim Arbury, Dr. Brent Elliott, George Lockie, Dr. Jim Quinlan, Brian Self, Jenny Vine, and, of course, the Internet.